ELL Activity Guide

Grade 3–6

Houghton
Mifflin
Harcourt

PROVIDES   Correlations to Chapter Content
INCLUDES   Copying Masters

Contents

Activities

Vocabulary Charts

How to Use the ELL Activity Guide

The ELL Activity Guide is designed to supplement English language acquisition for English Learners. The activities are designed to help students acquire math vocabulary and the language and writing skills necessary to communicate and understand math concepts. The activities will also help students progress through the language proficiency levels to gain fluency.

The ELL Activity Guide also provides support for assessing your students as they progress through the language proficiency levels and for providing effective teaching for English Learners.

Strategies for Effective Language Teaching

Create a Supportive Environment English Learners come from different linguistic, cultural, and social backgrounds, and bring a variety of educational needs to the classroom. Teachers need to be sensitive to those needs and establish an environment where all students feel safe and free to take risks.

Create Comprehensible Input Teachers can provide comprehensible input through the use of gestures, appropriate speech rate, dramatization, visuals, realia, and hands-on activities using manipulatives, charts, repetition, and rephrasing.

Encourage Student Interaction Because of the social nature of language learning, students need continual opportunities for interaction, both student-to-student and teacher-to-student. Provide English Learners with frequent opportunities to interact with native English speakers.

Build Background Working with examples and problems drawn from the various content areas requires students to constantly build on their knowledge base. Teachers need to ask, "What prerequisite knowledge do my students need in order to comprehend and learn this new material?" Video clips, pictures, magazines, trade books, and printed materials in students' primary language can all be used to provide the background knowledge needed for success.

Tap Prior Knowledge English Learners bring unique experiences and backgrounds to the classroom. To assist them in building meaning from these experiences and backgrounds, teachers need to help them connect what they know to new concepts being taught.

Teach Study and Reference Skills To be successful in learning content-area material, students need organizational skills. Using graphic organizers to gather and organize information helps students see comparisons, connections, and relationships between concepts, ideas, and words.

Provide for Primary Language Support English Learners who do not receive formal content-area instruction in their primary language need support. Teachers can use peer and cross-age tutors as well as parents and community volunteers. If a paraprofessional is available to provide primary language support, have them preview the upcoming lesson in the students' primary language. After the lesson is taught by the teacher in English, have the paraprofessional review the lesson to identify any misunderstandings that could be related to language barriers.

> *Instruction, not content, needs to be modified to meet the needs of English Learners. Content must remain rigorous.*

Effective Instructional Strategies

The activities in the ELL Activity Guide are based around instructional strategies that will help teachers assess students' mathematics knowledge and help students communicate about math on their current language proficiency level.

These instructional strategies are as follows.

Illustrate Understanding Students illustrate or sketch to communicate their understanding. Students can share their understanding through pictures and acquire new vocabulary by matching words to picture definitions.

Scaffold Language Through guided modeling and questions, students communicate understanding of a thing, situation, or process to demonstrate verbally or in writing what they already know or what they have learned.

Identify Relationships Students identify relationships between concepts and words to connect new information to prior knowledge.

Understand Context Students identify and experience vocabulary in context to clarify the meanings of words, idioms, and colloquial expressions. They can also explore synonyms and homophones to help distinguish math words from everyday words that have a similar meaning or sound the same.

Develop Meanings Students define words by using them in context with definitions or by matching words or visuals to their definitions.

Rephrase After hearing or reading a passage, students rewrite or verbally rephrase the passage in their own words. Students demonstrate their summary skills and ability to find important information.

Model Language Spoken and written language is demonstrated for students and repeated by students to practice pronunciation, sentence structure, and spelling.

Language Proficiency Levels

Researchers have identified three stages of development through which learners of a language progress.

Emerging Students at the Emerging level must be provided substantial linguistic support. They may understand some English, but they won't speak or write very much. Teachers can check understanding by asking students to point to things, use other gestures, or draw. As their skills develop, students begin to produce one- or two-word answers voluntarily. They are still building vocabulary, but to a question such as "Who is older, Carlos or Cathy?" they can answer, "Carlos."

Help students progress through the Emerging level by giving simple, clear directions and using gestures and facial expressions to convey meaning. Be sure to model correct English sentence structure and pronunciation and provide many hands-on experiences.

Expanding At this level, students begin to use short sentences. If the teacher asks, "Which number is greater, 396 or 254?" students may answer, "396 is greater." Students still use imprecise language and many nonstandard forms, but they say more, and they are moving toward standard English.

Students at the Expanding level can follow more complex directions. They need opportunities to use academic math vocabulary and concepts in interactive small- and whole-group discussions.

Bridging Students at the Bridging level are able to communicate in ways that are appropriate to different tasks, purposes, and audiences. They are transitioning to full engagement in grade-level academic tasks and activities without the need for specialized instruction.

At the Bridging level, students will be able to read and write with some fluency. They should be encouraged to justify and explain their work using academic language.

> *Keeping the levels of English proficiency in mind can help teachers tailor instructional practices so that students have the best possible environment for learning English.*

Assessing Language Development

No single tool can accurately measure a student's level of language proficiency and development. Frequent, informal observation of student behavior and work is necessary to form an accurate picture. The following tips and tools can help you observe and evaluate student performance.

Informal Assessment Tips

- Allow **sufficient time** for students to respond.

- If a student's response is inappropriate or inadequate, try **rephrasing** your question.

- Observe students in **situations** in which they are **comfortable.** For example, some students are more comfortable in small groups than in whole-class situations.

- Observe students at **different times**, on **different tasks**.

Informal Assessment Tools

Keeping **Math Journals** helps students practice their communication skills and provides teachers with a valuable resource to assess those skills. Encourage students to record questions, understandings, examples, and illustrations.

Student Assessment Checklist

The checklist on pages viii–x will help you evaluate students at different levels of language development.

Periodically use the checklist to evaluate a student's current language proficiency level to match students to the activities they should complete.

Student Assessment Checklist

Student's Name _____ Date _____

To evaluate a student's progress, observe behaviors at different times. Use a plus (+) or minus (−) symbol to indicate that the student has or has not exhibited the behavior.

		+ or −	Comments
Emerging			
Listening	Comprehends frequently occurring words and phrases		
	Follows simple directions		
	Comprehends some whole-class instruction		
	Begins to follow group discussions		
Speaking	Responds nonverbally by gesturing and imitating		
	Uses everyday, basic vocabulary		
	Makes short, appropriate oral responses to questions		
	May exhibit frequent errors in pronunciation		
Reading	Reads brief texts with simple sentences, supported by graphics or pictures		
Writing	Illustrates to convey meaning and ideas		
	Writes familiar words or phrases		
	Writes collaboratively		
	May exhibit frequent errors in grammar and writing conventions		

Student Assessment Checklist

Student's Name _____ **Date** _____

To evaluate a student's progress, observe behaviors at different times. Use a plus (+) or minus (−) symbol to indicate that the student has or has not exhibited the behavior.

		+ or −	Comments
	Expanding		
Listening	Understands most of what is said, in contextualized settings		
	Follows a series of directions		
Speaking	Responds using short sentences		
	Initiates simple conversations		
	May exhibit fairly frequent errors in pronunciation and grammar		
Reading	Reads texts with simple sentences independently		
Writing	Writes expanded vocabulary to provide extended responses		
	Writes short sentences		
	May exhibit fairly frequent errors in grammar and writing conventions		

Student Assessment Checklist

Student's Name _____ **Date** _____

To evaluate a student's progress, observe behaviors at different times. Use a plus (+) or minus (−) symbol to indicate that the student has or has not exhibited the behavior.

		+ or −	Comments
	Bridging		
Listening	Comprehends many abstract topics		
	Begins to recognize language subtleties		
Speaking	Expresses increasingly complex ideas using more elaborated discourse		
	Formulates and asks questions		
	May exhibit some errors in that do not usually impede meaning		
Reading	Reads increasingly complex text at grade level		
	Reads technical text supported by pictures or graphics		
Writing	Writes to meet increasingly complex academic demands		
	Paraphrases		
	Writes independently		

Grade 3 Chapter Correlation

Use the following correlation to determine which leveled activities best fit the math in each Grade 3 chapter.

	Emerging	Expanding	Bridging
Chapter 1	2, 3, 8, 19, 20, 21, 22, 37, 44, 49	5, 23, 24, 25, 42, 47	15, 16, 18, 34, 43, 48, 57, 59, 60
Chapter 2	2, 20, 21, 22, 49	11, 40, 41, 42, 46, 47	15, 16, 43, 57
Chapter 3	2, 7, 20, 22, 31, 36, 49, 50	25, 42, 45, 46, 47	6, 15, 16, 18, 43
Chapter 4	2, 20, 22, 31, 36, 49, 50	40, 42, 45, 46, 47	6, 15, 16, 18, 29, 43, 48, 57
Chapter 5	2, 8, 20, 22, 36, 50	46, 47	6, 15, 16, 18, 30, 60
Chapter 6	2, 20, 21, 22, 49	25, 33, 42, 46, 47	6, 15, 16, 18, 29, 43, 48
Chapter 7	2, 20, 22, 36, 49, 50	45, 46, 47	6, 15, 16, 18, 29, 35, 43, 48
Chapter 8	2, 3, 19, 20, 22, 31	25, 42, 45, 46, 47	15, 16, 18, 43
Chapter 9	2, 3, 20, 22, 44	24, 25, 46, 47	15, 16, 29
Chapter 10	1, 2, 20, 21, 22, 31, 39	12, 13, 24, 28, 40, 42, 46, 47, 52	6, 15, 16, 18, 35, 43, 48, 57
Chapter 11	2, 20, 21, 22, 44	40, 42, 54, 55	6, 15, 18, 43, 48, 57, 58, 60
Chapter 12	2, 20, 21, 22, 39, 44	10, 25, 26, 27, 40, 42, 55, 56	6, 18, 43, 57, 59

Grade 4 Chapter Correlation

Use the following correlation to determine which leveled activities best fit the math in each Grade 4 chapter.

	Emerging	Expanding	Bridging
Chapter 1	2, 3, 8, 19, 20, 37	11, 23, 24, 42, 47	15, 16, 18, 29, 34, 43, 57
Chapter 2	2, 8, 20, 22, 36, 44, 50	40, 42, 46, 47	6, 15, 16, 18, 29, 35, 43, 48
Chapter 3	2, 8, 19, 20, 22	46, 47	15, 16, 18, 29, 30, 43, 48, 60
Chapter 4	2, 8, 19, 20, 21, 36, 44, 50	33, 40, 42, 46, 47	15, 16, 18, 29, 30, 43, 48
Chapter 5	2, 19, 20, 22, 36, 50	25, 26, 27, 40, 42	6, 18, 43, 59, 60
Chapter 6	2, 3, 19, 20, 21, 22	25, 26, 40, 42	6, 18, 43, 60
Chapter 7	2, 3, 8, 19, 20, 21, 31	42, 45, 46, 47	6, 15, 16, 18, 35, 43, 48, 60
Chapter 8	2, 8, 19, 20, 22	25	6, 43, 60
Chapter 9	2, 3, 8, 19, 22, 31, 38, 44	9, 23, 27, 42, 53	15, 16, 17, 43
Chapter 10	2, 4, 20, 21, 22, 39	5, 10, 25, 27, 40, 42, 55, 56	6, 43, 57, 59
Chapter 11	2, 20, 21, 22, 31	24, 40, 42, 55	6, 43
Chapter 12	1, 2, 20, 21, 22, 31, 39	24, 40, 41, 42, 52, 54	18, 34, 35, 43, 48, 60
Chapter 13	2, 20, 21	40, 42, 54	6, 15, 18, 29, 43, 48, 59, 60

Grade 5 Chapter Correlation

Use the following correlation to determine which leveled activities best fit the math in each Grade 5 chapter.

	Emerging	Expanding	Bridging
Chapter 1	2, 8, 19, 20, 21, 22, 36, 37, 44	23, 25, 33, 40, 42, 46, 47	6, 14, 15, 16, 18, 29, 30, 34, 43, 57, 59, 60
Chapter 2	2, 20, 21, 44	33, 42, 46, 47	15, 16, 29, 43
Chapter 3	2, 3, 8, 19, 38, 44	5, 9, 23, 24, 42, 53	15, 16, 17, 29, 35, 59
Chapter 4	2, 7, 8, 20, 22, 38	5, 47	6, 18, 43, 59, 60
Chapter 5	2, 8, 19, 20, 38	42	18, 43, 59, 60
Chapter 6	2, 20, 22, 31, 36, 44	25, 26, 42, 45, 46, 47	6, 15, 16, 18, 35, 43, 48, 60
Chapter 7	2, 8, 19, 20, 21	24	6, 34, 43, 59, 60
Chapter 8	2, 8	33, 42	6, 15, 16, 29, 35, 43, 59, 60
Chapter 9	2, 20, 21, 22, 39	40, 41, 42	15, 16, 43, 60
Chapter 10	1, 2, 20, 21, 39	24, 28, 40, 42, 54	6, 34, 35, 43
Chapter 11	2, 20, 21, 22, 39	10, 25, 40, 42, 45, 55, 56	6, 18, 34, 43, 48, 57, 59, 60

Grade 6 Chapter Correlation

Use the following correlation to determine which leveled activities best fit the math in each Grade 6 chapter.

	Emerging	Expanding	Bridging
Chapter 1	2, 7, 8, 19, 20, 22, 36, 38, 50	23, 25, 26, 33, 40, 42, 45, 47, 53	15, 16, 17, 18, 35, 43, 60
Chapter 2	2, 3, 19, 20, 21, 22, 38	24, 33, 40, 42, 47	6, 15, 16, 18, 43, 48, 57, 59, 60
Chapter 3	2, 3, 19, 20, 22, 31	40, 42	6, 15, 18, 43, 57, 60
Chapter 4	2, 20, 21, 22	11, 24, 25, 40, 42, 46, 47	6, 15, 16, 18, 35, 43, 48, 57, 59, 60
Chapter 5	2, 20, 22, 31, 36	11, 46	6, 15, 16, 18, 35, 48, 59, 60
Chapter 6	2, 20, 21, 39	40, 42	6, 15, 16, 18, 29, 43, 48, 60
Chapter 7	2, 21, 36, 39	40, 42	14, 18, 30, 35, 43, 60
Chapter 8	2, 8, 20, 22, 44	33, 42	6, 14, 15, 16, 17, 18, 43, 48, 60
Chapter 9	2, 20	5, 42, 46, 47	6, 15, 16, 18, 43, 48, 60
Chapter 10	2, 20, 39	10, 40, 42	18, 43, 48, 59, 60
Chapter 11	2, 20, 21, 44	10, 27, 42, 55	6, 34, 43, 57
Chapter 12	2, 20, 21	40, 42, 46	15, 16, 18, 35, 43, 48, 59, 60
Chapter 13	2, 20, 22	5, 42	6, 18, 43, 59, 60

STRATEGY
Illustrate Understanding

Telling Time

Level: Emerging

Skills: Speaking, Reading, Writing

Objective: Draw clocks showing given times

Materials: index cards, paper, pencil, blank clock faces or circles to trace

Activity Have each student in the group write 2 times of day on index cards, one time per card. (The teacher may choose to write the times instead, 6–8 cards per group.)

Place all of the cards upside down on the table. One student turns over a card, and all of the students in the group draw an analog clock showing the time.

After everyone has drawn a clock, students compare drawings to check each other's work. Have students practice asking, **What time is it?** Others in the group answer, **It is four twenty-five.**

Repeat with the rest of the time cards.

Leveling: Expanding Have students specify A.M. or P.M., and then tell something that they do at that time of day.

Draw to Explain

Level: Emerging

Skills: Listening, Speaking

Objective: Practice drawing and describing diagrams

Materials: paper, crayons or color pencils

Activity Have partners sit together and draw a diagram to explain something such as a math problem or concept, a story, or an event. Have them use simple shapes that will be easy to discuss.

When they have finished their drawings, have partners explain their pictures by answering specific questions such as **Where is the goal?** or **What shape is the court?** Students at the Emerging level will point or respond in short answers.

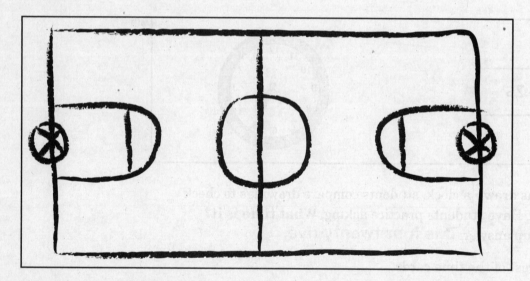

Leveling: Expanding Have partners sit back-to-back and draw to explain something that is familiar to them. Have them use simple shapes that will be easy to describe.

When each student is finished with his or her drawing, give each student a new sheet of paper. Have partners take turns describing their drawings so that the other student can draw it without seeing it. Have the students compare drawings, discuss the differences (if there are any), and talk about other ways they could have described their drawings.

Number Lines

Level: Emerging

Skills: Listening, Speaking, Writing

Objective: Order whole numbers, fractions, or decimals on a number line

Materials: index cards, paper, pencil

Activity Have each pair of students draw a long number line on a piece of paper. The students should make 21 tick marks on the number line and label only the first and last ticks.

Next, each student writes 5 numbers from 0–40 on index cards. All of the cards are turned upside down on the table.

Students take turns turning over a card and placing it at the correct position on the number line. Students should label each number on the number line.

Encourage discussion as students order numbers: they can state that the number is less than or greater than another number, to the left or right of another number, and so on. Have students check each other's work.

Tailor the activity to use numbers students are currently studying. Students can find numbers in the thousands, ten thousands, or hundred thousands, or can use number lines to order fractions, mixed numbers, or decimals.

Leveling: Expanding When a student picks up a number card, he or she reads the number aloud and the other student labels it on the number line without looking at the card.

Symmetrical Street Signs

Level: Emerging

Skills: Listening, Speaking

Objective: Identify and draw lines of symmetry

Materials: Symmetrical Street Signs Blackline Master, p. 86; pencil

Activity Give each partner a copy of the Symmetrical Street Signs Blackline Master. Have partners decide which of the street signs have line symmetry, and then draw the lines on the figures that are symmetrical.

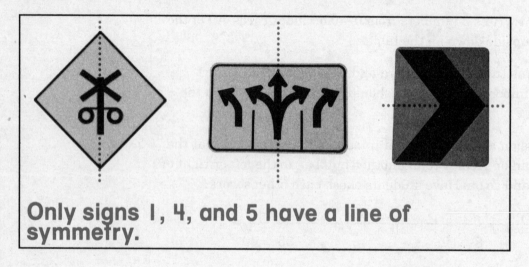

Only signs 1, 4, and 5 have a line of symmetry.

Ask students questions to guide their discussion of symmetry. Have students identify if the signs have more than one line of symmetry and explain or show why not.

Have students make up and draw a street sign that has a line of symmetry.

Leveling: Expanding Point out that some signs, such as the railroad crossing sign, are not symmetrical because of the letters or numbers. Have students discuss this, and ask them what needs to be removed from the sign to make it symmetrical. **If the letters and numbers are removed, signs 2 and 6 have multiple lines of symmetry, and sign 7 has one line of symmetry.**

STRATEGY
Illustrate
Understanding

Recognize Patterns

Level: Expanding

Skills: Listening, Speaking

Objective: Identify and explain patterns

Materials: Recognize Patterns Blackline Master, p. 87; pencil

Activity Give each partner a copy of the Recognize Patterns Blackline Master. Partners work together to find what comes next in each pattern. Emphasize that students should also describe the patterns verbally to each other.

The number of triangles increases by one each time, so five triangles will be next.

Even though many of the patterns will seem simple to some students, it can be difficult to verbally describe the patterns.

Extension After discussing the ten patterns, have students make up four patterns each—two using pictures and two using numbers. Have partners trade patterns and find the next term for each pattern.

Leveling: Emerging Have students find the next term for each pattern. Then, model how to describe the pattern verbally, and have students repeat the description.

Review Sheet

Level: Bridging

Skills: Listening, Speaking, Writing

Objective: Name, draw, and describe math words

Materials: paper; pencil; list of 6–10 words, use the vocabulary charts, pages 61–85, or vocabulary from the chapter

Activity Have students work in pairs to make a three-columned table like the one shown.

Give students a list of vocabulary words they are studying. Word lists should be for geometry, measurement, fractions, decimals, or other topics they can represent graphically.

Have students write the word, then work together to draw a picture and then write a description of the picture or definition of the word.

Word	Picture	Definition
square	□	• has four equal sides • has four right angles • has two pairs of parallel sides

Students should focus on discussing the characteristics and working together to complete the table.

Extension Have students quiz each other. One student reads a definition from the table, then the other student names or draws the word being described.

Leveling: Expanding Provide resources so that students can look up the definitions of the words.

STRATEGY
Scaffold Language

STRATEGY
Scaffold Language

How Much Money Is It?

Level: Emerging

Skills: Speaking, Writing

Objective: Calculate sums of money

Materials: play coins, cup, number cube, paper, pencil

Activity Have students choose a coin (or collection of coins) from the cup without looking and then roll a number cube.

Have partners take turns saying the value. For example, if they choose a nickel and roll a 4, they should state the value of 4 nickels. **20¢**

Students should record the coin(s), the number rolled, and the value on their paper.

Next, students return the coin(s) to the cup and repeat. They should play ten rounds, making sure to record their results each time.

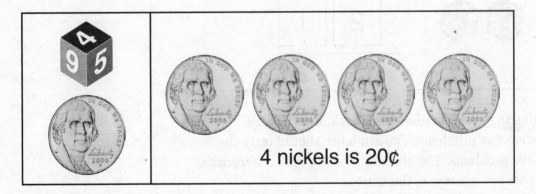

4 nickels is 20¢

This activity can be played as a game. Students take turns, and whoever has a greater total amount of money after five turns is the winner.

Leveling: Expanding Have one student choose a coin and roll a number cube without his or her partner seeing. The student then says the value.

The partner then has to guess which coin was chosen and which number was rolled. The partner can ask questions to help guess the correct coin and number.

Number Cube Operations Game

Level: Emerging
Skills: Speaking, Writing
Objective: Students practice operating with numbers
Materials: number cubes, pencil, paper

Activity Begin by choosing an operation and the size of the numbers in the problem. For example, you may choose two-digit subtraction.

Have students take turns rolling number cubes to generate the digits in a two-digit subtraction problem. Students then create a problem using the numbers they rolled.

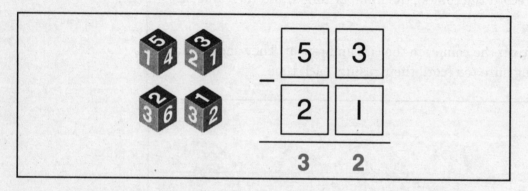

Have students solve the problem and check each other's work. Partners should each complete five problems. The students should tally the answers to their five problems. The student whose sums, differences, products or quotients are greater is the winner.

You can vary the number of digits in the problem and the operation depending on the math level of the players.

Leveling: Expanding Have students explain how they decided where to place each digit in the problem. Then have them find out if there is a way to use the same digits to get a greater answer or a lesser answer.

STRATEGY
Scaffold Language

How Many Coins Do I Need?

Level: Expanding

Skills: Listening, Speaking, Writing

Objective: Find combinations of coins to equal a given total

Materials: pencil, paper, play coins

Activity Have each student list five money amounts that are less than $1. Partners trade papers and write down the fewest number of coins needed to make each amount of money. They should also write or draw which coins to use.

1. $0.45	3 coins	
2. $0.13		
3. $0.75		

Students trade papers again to check each other's work. If they disagree on an answer, they should discuss it. They should ask each other questions, such as, **Which problem was the most difficult? Which was the easiest? Why?**

Extension Students work together to explain how they can be sure that their answers use the fewest number of coins possible. **If they have 2 dimes and a nickel, they should trade them for a quarter; if they have 2 nickels, they should trade them for a dime; if they have 5 pennies, they should trade them for a nickel.**

Leveling: Emerging Ask only questions about the coins that can be answered with a word or short phrase.

Characteristics of Shapes

Level: Expanding

Skills: Speaking, Reading, Writing

Objective: Identify characteristics of plane shapes or solids

Materials: 5 pictures of shapes or solids, paper, pencil

Activity Give students pictures of five shapes. Have students complete the sentence frame for each shape.

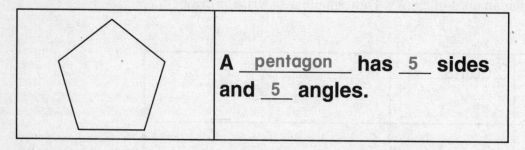

A __pentagon__ has _5_ sides and _5_ angles.

The sentence frame can be adapted to match the math students are currently studying. For example, you may want to include the number of diagonals, or the measurements of the angles.

If you give students pictures of a solid, the sentence frame may be:

A _____ has ____ vertices, ____ edges, and ____ faces.

Students should take turns completing the sentences and reading them aloud.

Extension Have students make observations about the figures. They may say, for example, **A square has one more angle than a triangle,** or **The number of angles is always equal to the number of sides.**

Leveling: Emerging Provide a word bank for the names of the figures.

STRATEGY
Scaffold Language

Comparing Classes

Level: Expanding

Skills: Listening, Speaking

Objective: Ask and answer questions to describe situations

Materials: none

Activity Provide partners the class information and the following questions. Have them take turns asking and answering questions about the two classes.

Mr. Lee teaches 3rd grade. Mr. Lee's class has 10 girls and 14 boys. The students are using computers and are drawing.	Miss Rivera teaches 5th grade. Miss Rivera's class has 17 girls and 9 boys. The students are all working on a science project.

1. Which class has more girls than boys? **Miss Rivera's**

2. Which class has fewer boys? **Miss Rivera's**

3. Which class has fewer students? **Mr. Lee's**

4. In which class are the students doing more activities? **Mr. Lee's**

5. In which class are the students older? **Miss Rivera's**

Students should answer the questions in phrases or complete sentences that use *-er* adjectives, *more than,* and *fewer than.*

Extension Have partners make up other information about the classes and ask questions to compare that information. Suggest that they describe how many students are wearing sneakers in each class, how many students brought lunch, or which class has taller students.

Leveling: Emerging Read the questions to them and then have them answer, "Mr. Lee's class" or "Miss Rivera's class."

Ramona's Schedule

Level: Expanding
Skills: Speaking, Writing
Objective: Describe events on a calendar
Materials: Calendar Blackline Master, page 88; pencil

Activity Give each student a copy of the Calendar Blackline Master. Have each student in the group write the dates on the calendar and then label the calendar with ten events. These events can be real or fictional.

Ramona's Schedule for October

Sunday	Monday	Tuesday	Wednesday	Thursday	Friday	Saturday
		1 Dentist	2	3	4 Football game	5
6	7	8	9	10 English test	11	12 Rake leaves
13	14	15 Math test	16	17	18	19 Picnic
20 Aquarium	21	22	23	24	25 Birthday party	26
27	28 Bake Sale	29	30 Mow lawn	31		

Next, have students swap papers and take turns saying sentences that describe events on the calendar. For example, **Ramona takes a math test on October 15.** Help students write their sentences.

Extension Ask students questions such as, **How many days after Ramona goes to the football game does she rake the leaves?** 8 days or **How many weeks after the football game is the birthday party?** 3 weeks

Leveling: Emerging Ask questions and have students answer with the day of the week. For example, **What day does Ramona mow the lawn?** Wednesday

STRATEGY
Scaffold
Language

Make a Schedule

Level: Expanding

Skills: Listening, Reading, Writing

Objective: Place events correctly on a calendar

Materials: Calendar Blackline Master, page 88; pencil

Activity Give each pair of students a copy of the Calendar Blackline Master. Tell them to write any month at the top of the page, and to number the days starting on any day in the first week. Be sure that students write the correct number of days for the month.

Have partners take turns reading the following sentences. While one partner reads, the other partner writes the activity on the correct date.

1. On the first Thursday of the month, Elena goes to a party.
2. On the second Friday, Elena has a doctor's appointment.
3. On the third Tuesday, she has a dentist's appointment.
4. On the fourth Monday, Elena takes her dog to the vet.
5. On the first Sunday, she has a family dinner.
6. On the last Saturday, her family cleans the yard.
7. Every Wednesday after school, Elena walks the dog.
8. On the third Wednesday, Elena goes to the library.
9. On the second and fourth Mondays, she has a computer class.
10. On the last day of the month, Elena takes a math test.

Extension Students ask each other questions about the calendar after all the events are filled in. For example, **What event happens on December 8?** and **What is the date when Elena goes to the library?**

Leveling: Emerging Review the words *first, second, third, fourth,* and *last*. Then read the questions aloud, reviewing unknown vocabulary as you go. Have students write down new vocabulary words.

Words to Equations

Level: Bridging

Skills: Reading, Writing

Objective: Translate math sentences into equations

Materials: paper, pencil

Activity Give each pair of students a list of sentences that can be translated into equations. Samples are given below.

1. The number of boys minus 10 is 15.	$b - 10 = 15$
2. The number of girls is 11 plus 12.	$g = 11 + 12$
3. The price is $16 more than $25.	$p = \$25 + \$16$
4. The price take away $25 equals $100.	$p - \$25 = \$100$
5. The time plus 2 hours is 8 hours.	$t + 2 = 8$
6. The time equals 2 hours added to 10 hours.	$t = 10 + 2$
7. The number of apples minus 3 is 7.	$a - 3 = 7$
8. The number of soccer balls is 4 less than 7.	$s = 7 - 4$

Students take turns reading the sentences aloud and then translating them into equations. Tell students to:

- use a letter to stand for the number they don't know
- use = for the words *is* or *equals*
- use − for words meaning subtraction (less, minus, take away)
- use + for words meaning addition (more than, plus, added to)

Extension Students make up their own sentences for their partners to translate into equations.

Leveling: Expanding Model several examples for students, and then let them finish on their own.

14

Understand Details

Level: Bridging

Skills: Listening, Reading

Objective: Answer questions about a passage

Materials: none

Activity Have students read the following passage or another grade-level appropriate passage based on the math they are studying. Suggest that students write down important information as they read.

> The 5th-grade students at Orange Grove Elementary need to raise money for their science trip. The class is going to the Florida Keys for one week in October to study marine life. There are three 5th-grade classes with twenty students in each class. The cost for the trip is $240 per student. In September, students sold magazines as a fundraiser for the trip. This month, parents are holding a Bake Sale fundraiser. They want to raise $1,800 so that each student will have $30 more to put toward the trip.

Ask questions based on the passage, such as:

- How many students are in the 5th grade at Orange Grove Elementary? **60**
- How long will the students stay in the Florida Keys? **I week**
- How much does the science trip cost per student? **$240**
- What month are the students going on the trip? **October**
- If Felicia has raised $140 from fundraisers, how much more does she need for the trip? **$100**

Extension Have partners write a story paragraph and questions for classmates to answer.

Leveling: Expanding Read the paragraph with students. Help them underline and make a list of important information. Have them look at their list to help answer questions about the story.

STRATEGY
Scaffold Language

Understand Story Problems

Level: Bridging

Skills: Listening, Reading

Objective: Answer questions about a passage

Materials: none

Activity Have students read the following passage or another grade-level appropriate passage based on the math they are studying. Suggest that students write down important information as they read.

> Ace Computer Company (ACC) has to decide which kind of transportation to use. They have to ship 50 computers before the end of the month. Trucks are not expensive and can travel anywhere. However, trucks can only travel 55 mph. Trains can go 75 mph, but trains do not go everywhere in the country. Planes are very fast. They travel about 200 mph. Sending a computer by plane costs twice as much as sending it by truck. Also, the nearest airport is 200 miles away from ACC. What should they do?

Ask questions based on the passage, such as:

- What does ACC make? **computers**
- Which type of transportation can go anywhere? **trucks**
- Which type of transportation is the fastest? **planes**
- Is ACC close to, far from, or next to an airport? **far from**
- How much faster can a train go than a truck? **20 mph**
- If it costs $50 to send a computer by truck, how much will it cost to send it by plane? **$100**

Extension Have partners write a story paragraph and questions for classmates to answer.

Leveling: Expanding Read the paragraph with students. Help them underline and make a list of important information. Have them look at their list to help answer questions about the story.

STRATEGY
Scaffold Language

Explain How to Add

Level: Bridging

Skills: Reading, Writing

Objective: Write a paragraph to explain the answer to a problem

Materials: paper, pencil

Activity Give partners the prices of 5 items. Tell students that they are going to buy two items for a friend's birthday. They have only $15 to spend.

Have students write a paragraph explaining:

- which items they chose
- why they chose those items
- how they calculated the total price of the two items
- how much money they will have left over

As part of their explanation, students should explain the process for adding and subtracting decimals, or for multiplying money amounts.

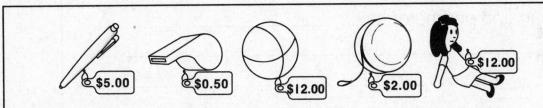

I will buy a ball and a yo-yo for my friend. I chose these because my friend will like them, and because they cost less than $15. Together, these cost $14. To add these, I started with $12 and then I counted up $2 more. I will have $1 left over.

Extension Students read their paragraphs aloud to the other students. Ask extension questions such as, **Name two items that you *cannot* buy for $15, and explain how you chose the items.**

Leveling: Expanding Provide sentence frames to help students write their paragraph. Students fill in key words to write their explanation.

STRATEGY
Scaffold Language

Write an Explanation

Level: Bridging
Skills: Reading, Writing
Objective: Write a definition and example
Materials: paper, pencil

Activity Tell students that they are going to write a letter to a friend named Jean who is learning about *perimeter*. (Tailor the activity to use any math concepts students are currently studying or have difficulty defining.)

Explain that in the letter, students need to explain to Jean what the word *perimeter* means and provide an example of how to find perimeter.

Dear Jean,

  I hear you are learning about perimeter. Don't worry—it is easy to find perimeter. First, you need to know the definition of perimeter. A perimeter is _____.

  You can find perimeter by _____.

  _____

  _____

  _____

  I hope my explanation helps you understand perimeter.
                                        Sincerely,
                                        _____

Students write their letters individually and then share them with their partners so they can compare the explanations.

Extension Have students read their letters out loud and then draw their example using a ruler and numeric expressions as necessary.

Leveling: Expanding Allow students to work with their partners to write a letter. Provide resources for them to use, such as their textbooks.

STRATEGY
Identify Relationships

Sort Numbers

Level: Emerging

Skills: Listening, Speaking

Objective: Sort a given set of numbers into categories

Materials: index cards, markers

Activity Provide each group of students with a set of numbers written on index cards. Give a rule for sorting the numbers.

For example, have students sort a set of numbers into the groups whole numbers, factions, and decimals.

Have students work together to sort the numbers into the specified categories.

Whole Numbers		Fractions		Decimals	
321	10	$\dfrac{3}{4}$	$\dfrac{1}{5}$	3.2	2.7
74	5	$\dfrac{1}{2}$	$\dfrac{2}{5}$	1.2	15.4
122		$\dfrac{2}{3}$		6.3	

Students can sort numbers by other categories such as:

- prime numbers and composite numbers
- even numbers and odd numbers
- numbers that are divisible by 5 and numbers that are not divisible by 5
- numbers that are perfect squares and numbers that are not perfect squares

Give students appropriate sets of numbers for each sorting activity.

Leveling: Expanding Have students write numbers on index cards and put them into two or three categories. Have other group members try to guess the categories.

Semantic Map

Level: Emerging

Skills: Speaking, Reading, Writing

Objective: Identify related vocabulary words by filling in a semantic map

Materials: Semantic Map Blackline Master, page 89; list of 6–10 words, use the vocabulary charts, pages 61–85, or vocabulary from the chapter

Activity Give partners a copy of the Semantic Map Blackline Master. Provide students with a topic and 6–10 vocabulary words. Have partners take turns selecting words that fit in the semantic map.

If there are fewer words, you can cover or color the extra spokes. (If there are more words, you can draw additional spokes.)

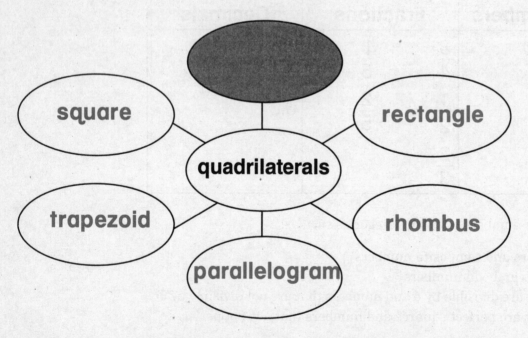

Students can copy the written words or place cards on the semantic map to show which words are related to the topic.

Leveling: Expanding Have partners think of vocabulary words that relate to the given topic. If students have difficulty thinking of some terms, provide terms they are studying. Allow students to explore how the terms you give them are like the ones they thought of on their own.

STRATEGY
Identify Relationships

Which Word Doesn't Belong?

Level: Emerging

Skills: Listening, Speaking, Reading

Objective: Decide which word doesn't belong

Materials: groups of 4–6 words, use the vocabulary charts, pages 61–85, or vocabulary from the chapter

Activity Give students groups of 4–6 vocabulary words. All of the terms should be related in some way except for one. Students choose the word that doesn't belong.

1.	inch	foot	mile	(meter)
2.	(yard)	centimeter	kilometer	meter
3.	mile	meter	inch	(liter)
4.	cup	pint	(milliliter)	quart
5.	milliliter	(gallon)	kiloliter	centiliter

Encourage students to discuss the meaning of each word to reinforce their decision. If they don't know the meaning of a word, provide them with a definition and examples. Have partners try to explain to each other before helping them.

Select vocabulary words for any math topic students are studying.

Leveling: Expanding Have students explain or write why the word they chose doesn't belong with the others. Students can complete the following sentence frames to help them discuss their choice.

____Meter____ does not belong.

____Meter____ is a word for ____metric length____.

The other words are for ____customary length____.

STRATEGY
Identify
Relationships

T-Chart

Level: Emerging

Skills: Reading, Writing

Objective: Practice vocabulary, making connections between new words and prior knowledge

Materials: list of 5–8 words, use the vocabulary charts, pages 61–85, or vocabulary from the chapter

Activity Draw a T-chart for a small group of students. Make sure they can all see the T-chart.

Provide students with 5–8 vocabulary words and two sorting categories. Some of the words should be related to one sorting category and the other words should be related to the other sorting category. Students then sort the words into the correct groups.

For example,

T-Chart	
Multiplication Words	Division Words
times factor product	quotient dividend divisor remainder

Encourage students to discuss the meaning of each word to reinforce their decision. If they don't know the meaning of a word, provide them with a definition and examples. Have students try to explain to each other before helping them.

Leveling: Expanding Select words that are more closely related, for example rhombus, square, trapezoid, and rectangle (figures that have equal sides—rhombus and square—and figures that do not have equal sides—trapezoid and rectangle). Intermediate students can work with 8–12 terms.

STRATEGY
Identify Relationships

Place Value

Level: Expanding

Skills: Listening, Speaking, Writing

Objective: Read and write numbers in a place-value chart

Materials: place-value chart, pencil

Activity Give students a place-value chart that reflects the place-value periods students have studied. Then give partners a list of 8–12 numbers.

Students take turns reading a number aloud, while their partner writes the number in the place-value chart.

For example,

thousands	hundreds	tens	ones
	3	7	4

374
25
1,004
407
3,118

Be sure to adjust the numbers and the place-value chart to match the place value your students are studying. The activity also can be adjusted to practice decimal place value.

Have students check each other's work as they go.

Then have partners ask each other questions such as **How many tens are in 374?** There are 7 tens in 374. **What is the value of 3 in 374?** The value is 300.

Extension After writing the numbers in the chart, students can read them in order from least to greatest.

Leveling: Emerging Read each number aloud or write it on the board. Have students repeat the number and then write it in the chart.

STRATEGY
Identify
Relationships

Comparative Sentences

Level: Expanding

Skills: Listening, Speaking, Reading, Writing

Objective: Compare numbers or lengths

Materials: index cards, markers, pencil

Activity Have students use sentence frames to compare numbers or lengths.

<u>Compare Numbers</u>: Have each partner make a set of 10–15 number cards. The numbers should be ones students are studying (which could include fractions or decimals).

Each partner draws a card. Partners then compare the numbers by using the sentence frames.

Is __107__ greater than __105__ ?

__107__ is greater than __105__ .

Is __107__ less than __105__ ?

__105__ is less than __107__ .

<u>Compare Lengths</u>: Have each partner make a set of 10 object cards.

Each partner draws a card. Partners then compare the lengths of the objects by using the sentence frames.

Is __a pencil__ longer than __a desk__ ?

__A desk__ is longer than __a pencil__ .

Extension Have students write their comparative sentences. Students can also compare the heights of people, the weights of objects, or the capacity of containers.

Leveling: Emerging The teacher asks students the comparative question. Students answer with *less than, greater than, shorter than, longer than,* etc.

STRATEGY
Identify
Relationships

Two-Circle Venn Diagram

Level: Expanding

Skills: Speaking, Writing

Objective: Sort shapes or words in a 2-circle Venn diagram

Materials: paper, markers, pencil

Activity Have partners draw two large overlapping circles to make an overlapping Venn diagram. Give students two sorting categories and then have them label each circle.

Venn diagrams can be used to sort and make connections among any math vocabulary students are studying.

For example, have students label the circles **Regular Shapes** and **Quadrilaterals**. Have partners work together to draw shapes in each part of the Venn diagram.

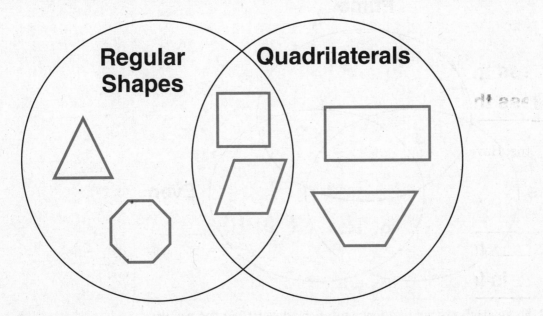

Extension Have students discuss how they sorted the shapes or words. Have them explain how the shapes or words that are grouped together are similar and why they are similar.

Leveling: Emerging Ask questions to help students identify why the shapes or words fit in each category.

Three-Circle Venn Diagram

Level: Expanding

Skills: Speaking, Writing

Objective: Sort shapes or numbers in a 3-circle Venn diagram

Materials: paper, pencil

Activity Have partners draw a three-circle Venn diagram. Give them three sorting categories and have them label each circle.

Venn diagrams can be used to sort and make connections among any math vocabulary students are studying.

For example, have students label the three circles **Prime**, **Even**, and **Multiples of 3**. Have students work together to write the numbers 2–12 in the correct part of the Venn diagram.

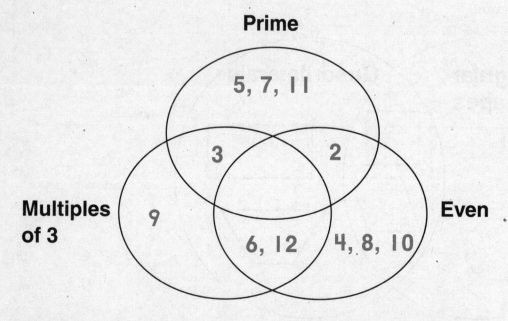

Extension Have students write a few sentences describing the results of their Venn diagram. Have them answer the question, **How did you decide which numbers went in the overlapping parts?**

Leveling: Emerging Ask questions as they sort the numbers to help them verbalize what they are doing. Ask questions that can be answered with a word or short phrase.

Which Diagram Is Best?

Level: Expanding

Skills: Speaking, Writing

Objective: Choose the best diagram to sort numbers and words

Materials: Venn Diagrams Blackline Master, page 90; pencil

Activity Give students a copy of the Venn Diagrams Blackline Master and a list of categories and items to sort.

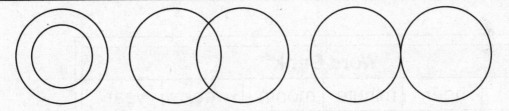

Odd numbers, Even numbers: 1, 2, 3, 4, 5, 6, 7, 8, 9, 10
Multiples of 2, Multiples of 3: 2, 4, 6, 8, 10, 12, 14, 16, 18, 20
Whole numbers, Even numbers: 1, 2, 3, 4, 5, 6, 7, 8, 9, 10

Have partners choose the best diagram for each set of items. Have them label and fill in the diagram.

Extension Give students a list of words or numbers. Have partners select two categories the items fit. Then have them choose the best diagram to sort the words or numbers. Have them label and fill in the diagram.

Students can sort lists such as:

• 4, 5, 8, 10, 12, 15, 16, 20, 24, 25, 28, 30, 32, 35, 36, 40

• circle, cube, cylinder, pyramid, rectangle, square, triangle

• equilateral, rectangle, rhombus, right, scalene, square

Leveling: Emerging Use only numbers, or use simple vocabulary that is reviewed before the activity. Model an example for the students. As students work, ask questions to help them verbalize the process.

Word Search: Measurements of Time

Level: Expanding

Skills: Reading, Writing

Objective: Find measurement words in a puzzle and use them in sentences

Materials: Word Search: Measurements of Time Blackline Master, p. 91; pencil

Activity Give each student a copy of the Word Search: Measurements of Time Blackline Master. Have students complete the puzzle and the sentences.

Word Bank					
day	hour	minute	month	week	year

```
Q  Y  M  G  E  Q  K  M
P  W  O  Y  E  A  R  B
B  P  N  H  O  U  R  X
M  D  T  J  H  W  A  C
S  A  H  P  U  E  A  I
B  Y  N  K  O  E  J  S
P  J  N  T  Q  K  F  B
M  I  N  U  T  E  F  Z
```

After the sheet is completed, have students take turns reading their sentences with a partner to check their work.

Extension Students can ask each other comparative questions using the words found in the puzzle. For example, **Which is longer, a minute or an hour?**

Leveling: Bridging Have students cover up the word bank as they solve the puzzle. Then have students write sentences about time, such as **I go to school 5 days each week.**

STRATEGY
Identify
Relationships

Just the Facts

Level: Bridging

Skills: Reading, Writing

Objective: Read story problems and decide which information is needed to solve each problem

Materials: paper, pencil

Activity Give students story problems that have unnecessary information. Have students read each situation and decide which information they *do not* need. Then ask them to write the information they *do* need on their paper.

For example,

---

1. Sam needs to buy enough baseball bats for all the members of his baseball team. He has $200. There are 10 players. ~~They have big feet.~~ How much can he spend for each baseball bat?

2. Jose needs $50 to buy a basketball. ~~His old one has a hole in it.~~ He is going to rake leaves for 10 hours at $6 per hour this weekend. Can he buy the basketball on Monday?

3. Ms. Chang wants to give 5 math tests this marking period. There are four months in the marking period. ~~One of the months is April.~~ Can she give only one test per month?

Students should write a summary sentence like this: **To find out how much Sam can spend for each bat, I need to know the amount of money he has and how many players are on his team.**

Extension Have students solve the problems.

Leveling: Expanding Read the problems aloud and discuss them with students. Then have students write the information needed to solve each problem.

STRATEGY
Identify Relationships

Where Does the + Go?

Level: Bridging

Skills: Speaking

Objective: Explore methods to solve problems and discuss addition and multiplication

Materials: paper, pencil

Activity Give pairs of students the following number puzzles. Have them work together to determine where to place the 3 plus signs to make each equation true. The multiplication problem underneath each equation is a hint.

1 5 0 + 1 5 0 + 7 5 + 7 5 15 × 30	= 450
2 0 0 + 5 0 + 4 0 + 1 0 12 × 25	= 300
4 0 0 + 1 4 0 + 4 0 + 1 4 22 × 27	= 594
6 0 0 + 2 0 + 1 2 0 + 4 24 × 31	= 744

Encourage students to discuss how they can test each equation. Help them make the connection between the addition equation and the multiplication problem to see that each addend is a product of the broken apart factors in the multiplication problem. For example, 15 × 30 is broken apart as (10 + 5) × (15 + 15).

Extension Have students break apart the factors in the multiplication problems so that they make the addends in each addition equation. Help students discuss the process of breaking apart factors so they are easier to multiply.

Leveling: Expanding Ask questions to guide the problem solving. Ask where the plus sign should go and then allow students to point to the location. Read the suggested equation and then have them repeat the equation to practice saying and reading equations. Help students test each equation.

Math Homophones

Level: Emerging

Skills: Listening, Speaking, Reading

Objective: Identify and use math words and their homophones

Materials: none

Activity Give students math words that sound like other words. (Some examples are provided below; tailor the activity to use words students are currently studying, have difficulty pronouncing, or confuse when they are spoken.)

Write EL some math words and their homophones (words that sound the same) on the board. Have students match the words that sound alike. Encourage students to either read the word aloud or repeat after you.

eight	ate	quart	court
four	for	sum	some
hour	our	two	to, too
one	won	weight	wait
plane	plain	whole	hole

Help students identify the math word in each pair and talk about the meanings of both words.

Leveling: Expanding Write the math word and its homophone in two sentences. Have students read aloud or repeat the sentences and focus on pronunciation.

Read one sentence and ask, **What does the word mean?** Have students respond with the meaning of the word in context. Read the second sentence and ask the same question. Have students focus on the different meanings of words that sound the same.

STRATEGY
Understand Context

Make Money Amounts

Level: Expanding

Skills: Speaking

Objective: Practice talking about and making money amounts

Materials: play bills and coins

Activity Give students a collection of coins and bills. Write down several money amounts such as $0.72, $1.22, $2.68, and $0.45. Have students make the money amounts in several different ways.

Have students explain how they made an amount by using the least number of bills and coins possible. Have them combine and trade coins of equal value if they have not made the amount with the least number of bills and coins.

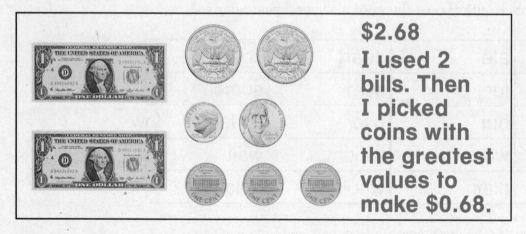

$2.68
I used 2 bills. Then I picked coins with the greatest values to make $0.68.

Extension Give students a collection of coins. Tell them the price of an item and then ask, **Do you have enough money?** Encourage students to count the coins out loud and discuss how they can make the amount using their coins.

If they do not have enough money, ask students to determine how much more they need. Have students discuss ways to find out how much more they need.

Take away or add some coins and give students a new price of an item. Again ask, **Do you have enough money?**

Leveling: Emerging Focus on counting the coins out loud. Have students show the coins and then help them say the names of the coins and count the coins to make the given amount.

STRATEGY
Understand Context

Multiplication and Division Clues

Level: Expanding

Skills: Listening, Speaking, Reading, Writing

Objective: Identify word clues for multiplication and division

Materials: paper, pencil

Activity Give students several multiplication and division story problems. Have them identify and circle the words that help them decide which operation to use to solve the problem.

Have students look for words that appear in several problems such as *group* or *equal group, divide,* and *each*.

Ask students to discuss how the words are used in each problem and to determine how to use these words to decide which operation is needed to solve the problem.

A teacher has 32 students in her classroom. She needs to (divide) them into 4 (equal groups). How many students are in (each group)?	There are 6 adults on the field trip. (Each) adult has a (group) of 9 students. How many students are on the field trip?
Division; 32 ÷ 4 = 8	Multiplication; 6 × 9 = 54

Have students identify if they should multiply or divide to solve the problem. Then, have students write an equation and solve the problem.

Extension Have students write their own multiplication and division word problems. Have each student write two problems and then read both problems to the group. Have the students identify words that help them decide which operation to use and then solve the problem.

Leveling: Emerging Read the problem and help students find the words that identify the operation as multiplication or division. Discuss how the words indicate the operation.

partners   15 minutes

Multiple Meanings

Level: Bridging

Skills: Listening, Reading, Writing

Objective: Identify and use words with multiple meanings

Materials: paper, pencil

Activity Give students math words that also have another meaning. (Some examples are provided below; tailor the activity to use words students are currently studying.)

Read the word and two or three definitions for the word. Have students write a sentence using each definition.

center	change	difference	expression
face	foot	key	kite
meter	multiple	net	odd
period	pound	product	round
scale	solution	volume	yard

Extension After students have written a sentence for each definition, have them trade papers with a partner. The partner circles the sentences that use the math definition of each word.

Leveling: Expanding Read a word and two definitions. Have students select the math definition by raising their hands. Have them write the math definition as you read it.

STRATEGY
Understand Context

Math Storyteller

Level: Bridging

Skills: Speaking

Objective: Practice vocabulary by telling stories

Materials: 3 related pictures

Activity Give students three pictures that are related in some way. For example, give them a picture of a carnival, a roller coaster, and a snack shop.

Have students tell a story using those pictures.

Next, have students think about the math in their stories. Ask students questions about numbers of things in their stories, the shape of something, or how tall something is. For example, ask them how many friends go to the carnival, how many friends can sit in one car on the roller coaster, and how tall the roller coaster is.

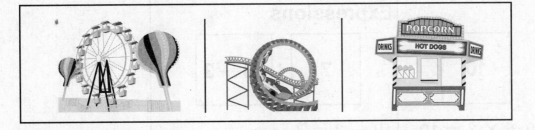

Extension Help students write a story problem to go along with their story. Use the math they are studying and the information from the story to pose a problem. Then solve the problem as a group.

Leveling: Expanding Tell the story in a round, with each student supplying some of the information. Help them structure the sentences and have the group repeat any difficult words. Provide some math vocabulary as they tell the story.

STRATEGY
Develop Meanings

Math Concentration

Level: Emerging

Skills: Listening, Speaking

Objective: Practice reading numbers and expressions

Materials: Math Concentration Multiples Blackline Master, p. 92; Math Concentration Expressions Blackline Master, p. 93; scissors

Activity Give students a copy of either the Math Concentration Multiples Blackline Master or the Math Concentration Expressions Blackline Master. Students cut out the cards, shuffle them, and turn them upside down.

Players take turns turning two cards over to see if they are a match. If a player turns over a match, the player keeps the cards and goes again. When there are no matches left, the player with the most cards wins.

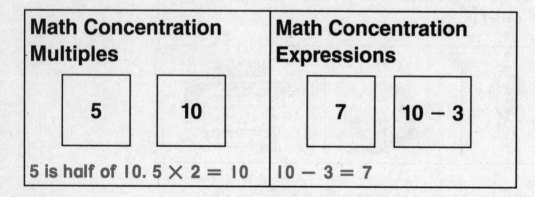

For Math Concentration Multiples, a match is a number and a card showing either half or twice that number. For example, **5** and **10** are a match. Have students say, **5 and 10 are a match. 5 is half of 10 (or 10 is twice as much as 5).**

For Math Concentration Expressions, a match is an expression and a number that is equal to that expression. Have students state the equality. For example, they can say, **10 − 3 and 7 are a match. 10 − 3 is equal to 7.**

Leveling: Expanding
Have students describe the relationship when they make a match. Have students play with a greater number of cards, for example, by writing expressions for the numbers 11–20.

© Houghton Mifflin Harcourt Publishing Company

partners   15 minutes

Whole Number Place Value

Level: Emerging

Skills: Listening, Speaking, Writing

Objective: Practice whole number place value vocabulary

Materials: Whole Numbers Blackline Master, p. 94; pencil

Activity Give each student a copy of the Whole Numbers Blackline Master. Read the directions, one row at a time. Have students circle the appropriate numbers on their sheets.

For row:	Ask students to circle all numbers that have:	Answers
1	a 4 in the tens place	B, E, F
2	an 8 in the ones place	A, D
3	a 3 in the hundreds place	B, E, F
4	a 1 in the thousands place	A, C, D, E
5	a 5 in the ones place	A, E, F
6	a 6 in the hundreds place	A, B, E
7	a 9 in the thousands place	A, F
8	a 5 in the tens place	C
9	a 2 in the ones place	A, B, C, E
10	a 0 in the tens place	A, C, E, F

Make up other directions to have students identify digits in other place-value positions.

Read a number by place value and have students write the correct number. For example, **three thousands, six hundreds seven ones. 3,607**

Leveling: Expanding Ask questions that require speaking rather than simply circling numbers. For example, **Read all of the numbers that have a 5 in the ones place,** or **What do the numbers 133, 331, and 139 have in common?** They all have a 3 in the tens place.

STRATEGY
Develop
Meanings

Decimal Place Value

Level: Emerging

Skills: Listening, Speaking, Writing

Objective: Practice decimal and whole number place value vocabulary

Materials: Decimals Blackline Master, p. 95; pencil

Activity Give each student a copy of the Decimals Blackline Master. Read the directions, one row at a time. Have students circle the appropriate numbers on their sheets.

Make sure to clearly pronounce the *–th* at the end of tenths, hundredths, and thousandths.

For row:	Ask students to circle all numbers that have:	Answers
1	a 4 in the tens place	D
2	a 6 in the hundredths place	A, E
3	an 8 in the ones place	B, D, E
4	a 9 in the thousandths place	B, C, E
5	a 3 in the hundreds place	A, F
6	a 5 in the tenths place	A, B, D
7	a 1 in the thousands place	A, C, D
8	a 2 in the ones place	A, B, C, E
9	a 5 in the tens place	C, D, E
10	a 0 in the tenths place	A, C

Read a number by place value and have students write the correct number. For example, **three thousands, six hundreds seven ones and four tenths.** 3,607.4

Leveling: Expanding Instead of using the directions listed, have students take turns making up and naming a rule for each row.

STRATEGY
Develop Meanings

Crossword Puzzles

Level: Emerging/Expanding

Skills: Reading, Writing

Objective: Complete crossword puzzles to practice math vocabulary

Materials: Crossword Puzzle Blackline Masters, pages 96–101

Activity Give each student a crossword puzzle to complete. Have them read the clues and determine which word matches the clue and fits in the space on the crossword puzzle.

Select a vocabulary list from the following crossword puzzles.

Emerging*	Expanding
Identify Plane Shapes, page 96	Symbols, page 99
Attributes of Plane Shapes, page 97	Graphs, page 100
Metric Unit Abbreviations, page 98	Customary Unit Abbreviations, page 101

*word bank provided

Leveling: Emerging Provide a word bank on the Expanding crossword puzzles. Students at the Emerging level may not be able to read the clues, so provide illustrations for each clue. For example:

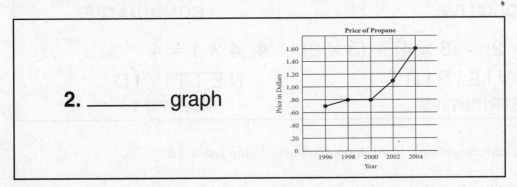

2. _____ graph

For students at the Expanding level, remove the word bank on the Emerging crossword puzzles.

Unscramble Math Words

Level: Expanding

Skills: Reading, Writing

Objective: Unscramble words to make math words

Materials: 4–5 words, use the vocabulary charts, pages 61–85, or vocabulary from the chapter

Activity Give students 4–5 vocabulary words. Scramble the letters in each word and write them on the board so that everyone can see them. Draw an illustration or write an example of each word so students have a visual definition of the word they are trying to unscramble. Students unscramble the letters to identify the vocabulary words.

Some examples are provided; tailor the activity to use words students are currently studying, or have difficulty spelling or reading.

Identify the shapes:

T O E P N A N G   T E L C R A G N E   R U Q A S E

PENTAGON   **RECTANGLE**   **SQUARE**

Identify the property:

1. $(5 + 8) + 4 = 5 + (8 + 4)$

E A C S S O I T I A V

ASSOCIATIVE

2. $4 \times 5 = 5 \times 4$

O C I T T U V E A M M

COMMUTATIVE

3. $3 \times (4 + 2) = (3 \times 4) + (3 \times 2)$

T D U B V I E I S I R T

DISTRIBUTIVE

4. $4 \times 1 = 4$

N E T T I Y I D

IDENTITY

Extension After unscrambling a word, have students define the word.

Leveling: Emerging Provide a word bank, and allow students to look up the word and repeat the definition.

STRATEGY
Develop Meanings

Recognize Graphs

Level: Expanding

Skills: Listening, Speaking, Reading,

Objective: Recognize and understand the differences between graphs

Materials: Recognize Graphs Blackline Master, p. 102; pencil

Activity Give each student a copy of the Recognize Graphs Blackline Master. Have them work as a group to unscramble the names of the types of graphs.

Ask questions to reinforce the differences and similarities among the different types of graphs.

---

1. Which graphs have an *x*-axis and a *y*-axis? **line graph, bar graph**

2. Which graph shows how something is divided up into separate parts? **circle graph**

3. Which graph shows how something changes over time? **line graph**

4. Which graphs are best for comparing data? **line plot, bar graph**

5. Which graph seems the most different from the others and why? **Answers will vary.**

Extension Have students decide which type of graph is best for different types of data. For example, say, **If I wanted to make a graph showing the temperature at different times during the day, which type of graph is best?** **line graph**

Leveling: Emerging If the questions are too difficult, have students make a list of things that are the same and things that are different about the various types of graphs.

Activity 42

partners   15 minutes

Math Definitions

Level: Expanding

Skills: Listening, Reading, Writing

Objective: Look up, dictate, and define vocabulary words

Materials: pencil; vocabulary charts, pages 61–85, or vocabulary from the chapter

Activity Have students write vocabulary words on index cards, one word per card. One student looks up and dictates the definition while the other student writes the definition on the back of the card.

Some examples are provided; tailor the activity to use words students are currently studying, or have difficulty reading or defining.

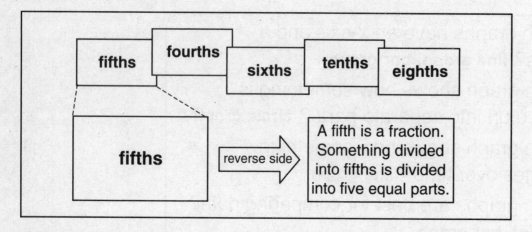

Extension Students should practice vocabulary by using these cards as flash cards.

Leveling: Emerging Help students write the definitions on the backs of the cards. Have them illustrate the definition when possible.

STRATEGY
Develop
Meanings

4-Square Vocabulary Grid

Level: Bridging

Skills: Reading, Writing

Objective: Practice vocabulary by defining

Materials: 4-Square Vocabulary Grids, page 103; vocabulary charts, pages 61–85, or vocabulary from the chapter

Activity Give students a copy of the 4-Square Vocabulary Grids Blackline Master and a list of 4–5 vocabulary words. Have partners take turns filling in a 4-Square Vocabulary Grid for each word.

First students write the word. Then they write what the word makes them think of. Then they look up and write the definition of the word. Finally, they write a sentence that uses the word.

The word	Makes me think of
Definition	**Sentence**

The 4-Square Vocabulary Grids can be used with any math vocabulary including fractions, geometry, measurement, or any terms that are new or confusing for students.

Extension Students can keep a folder or booklet containing all 4-Square Vocabulary Grids completed throughout the year. They can use the folder to review the vocabulary whenever time permits.

Leveling: Expanding Discuss and define words with the students.

small group   15 minutes

Math Synonyms

Level: Emerging

Skills: Listening, Speaking, Reading

Objective: Identify and use math words and their synonyms

Materials: index cards, markers

Activity Have students match common words to their math synonyms (math words that have the same meaning). (Some examples are provided below; tailor the activity to use words students are currently studying, or have difficulty pronouncing or recalling the definition.)

same value	equivalent	same shape	congruent
answer	solution	total	sum
guess	estimate	show	represent
information	data	corner	vertex
shape	plane figure	average	mean
around	perimeter	box	prism

Write each word on a separate index card. Shuffle the cards and then have students work as a group to match the synonyms.

After all the cards are matched, talk about the meanings of the words and give examples. Have students repeat the definitions and examples.

Leveling: Expanding
Have one student use the math word in a sentence..Then the others in the group name a synonym for the word used.

STRATEGY
Rephrase

Words for Quantities

Level: Expanding

Skills: Listening, Writing

Objective: Practice words for quantities

Materials: paper, pencil

Activity Have students practice words that describe quantities. Read aloud the words and meanings below.

Here are four words that mean **two** of something:

- **Pair** means two matching items, such as a *pair* of shoes.
- **Double** means twice as much of something. For example, if you roll two 6s, you roll *double* sixes.
- **Twin** means two of the same; such as *twin* boys, brothers who were born on the same day.
- **Couple** is an informal way of saying two. You can say, "I ate a *couple* of crackers."

Other quantity words include **dozen,** which means twelve of something, and **single,** which means one of something.

Then have partners complete a chart that lists the word, the number it represents, and how the word is used in a sentence. When the charts are complete, have students read their examples.

Word	Number	Example
Pair	2	I have a new pair of socks.
Dozen	12	I bought a dozen bagels.

Extension Have students make flash cards with the word on one side and a drawing of an example on the other side.

Leveling: Emerging Say and have students repeat the quantity words and then help them fill in the chart as a group.

STRATEGY
Rephrase

What's the Story?

Level: Expanding
Skills: Listening, Speaking, Reading, Writing
Objective: Listen to and rephrase the events of a story
Materials: paper, pencil

Activity Read the story (or another story related to the math students.
are currently studying). Have students listen carefully to the details.

> Luis and Maria wanted to make a CD holder for
> their parents. Their parents have 60 CDs. Luis and
> Maria drew a plan for a holder that has 3 shelves
> that are each big enough to hold 20 CDs.
>
> After they drew their plan, Luis and Maria went to
> the hardware store to buy the wood, nails, and paint
> for the CD holder.
>
> It took Luis and Maria two weeks to build the
> CD holder. They gave it to their parents for an
> anniversary present. Their parents were so happy!

Have each partner make a list of the events that take place in the story.
After each student has written a list, have partners discuss the lists and
make sure they have included all the important details.

Then have the partners rephrase the entire story in their own words.
Have them read the story again to compare their rephrased story to the
original story.

Leveling: Emerging Give each student a copy of the story and have
them read along with you. Help them identify and underline the events
and important information. Then make a list on the board of the events
and information that the students underlined.

STRATEGY
Rephrase

partners   15 minutes

What's the Problem?

Level: Expanding

Skills: Listening, Speaking, Writing

Objective: Listen to and rephrase a story problem

Materials: paper, pencil

Activity Read the story problem (or another problem related to the math students are currently studying). Have students make a list of the important information in the problem.

The Drama Club, which has 18 members, raised $60 for a party. Kayla, Mike, and Julia were each given $20 to buy supplies for the party.

Kayla bought cups for $3.95 and plates for $5.25. Mike bought 4 jugs of juice for $3.80 each. Julia spent a total of $19.05 on snack foods.

All but two members of the Drama Club attended the party.

How much money is left after buying the supplies? $16.55

How many people were at the party? 16

After listening to the problem, partners rephrase and then discuss the important information in the problem. Have them point out any unnecessary information from the problem as well.

Partners should then discuss how to solve each part of the problem. When they solve the problem, have them write their answers in complete sentences.

Leveling: Emerging Pass out copies of the problem, and list the important facts from the problem on the board as you discuss it. Model how to rephrase the problem.

STRATEGY
Rephrase

Rewrite

Level: Bridging

Skills: Reading, Writing

Objective: Practice writing an explanation

Materials: paper, pencil

Activity Have students read an explanation for a math process, like the example here for finding perimeter. Use any process students are currently studying, including solving multistep problems.

Perimeter is the distance around the outside edge of a shape. I will show you how to find the perimeter of a rectangle. A rectangle has two pairs of sides that are the same length.

First, measure the top of the rectangle. Write this measurement to label the length of the top. Write the same measurement to label the bottom, since it is the same length.

Next, measure and label the left side of the rectangle. Write the same measurement to label the right side, since it is the same length.

Finally, add the measures of all four sides. The total is the perimeter. Don't forget to include the units of measure!

Have students rewrite the explanation in their own words. Tell them to imagine that they are teaching a friend who does not know the math process they are describing. Have them include pictures to illustrate the steps and demonstrate their understanding.

Leveling: Expanding Discuss and demonstrate the procedure being described before partners rewrite the explanation in their own words.

How Many?

Level: Emerging

Skills: Listening, Speaking, Reading

Objective: Answer questions about how many

Materials: pattern blocks, classroom objects

Activity Arrange some pattern blocks or classroom objects in rows or groups. Each row or group should have the same shape or object.

Point to a row or group. Ask the question and model the language students should use to answer the question.

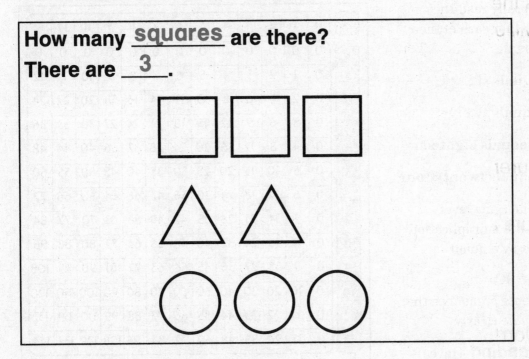

How many __squares__ are there?
There are __3__.

Then have students repeat the answer.

Students at the Emerging level may have difficulty answering the question in a complete sentence, so allow them to respond with just the number or with a hand gesture.

Change the number of pattern blocks or objects and repeat the activity.

Leveling: Expanding
Have students take turns asking and answering the question. Write the sentence frames for students to work independently.

STRATEGY
Model Language

small group   15 minutes

Multiplication Facts

Level: Emerging

Skills: Listening, Speaking

Objective: Practice saying multiplication facts

Materials: 12 × 12 multiplication table, index cards numbered 2–12, color pencils

Activity Give each student a 12 × 12 multiplication table and index cards numbered 2–12. Have each student choose an index card and color all of the multiples of that number on their multiplication chart.

Have students chorally read the multiplication facts for each of their numbers. For example,

Six times one equals six.

Six times two equals twelve.

Six times three equals eighteen.

Six times four equals twenty-four.

Students at the Emerging level may need to have the multiplication sentences modeled by a fluent English speaker.

Be sure that students pronounce the -*s* at the end of *equals* clearly.

Leveling: Expanding
Have partners take turns. One student points to a number on the table and then the other student looks on the table to determine the factors. The student should then say the multiplication fact.

×	0	1	2	3	4	5	6	7	8	9	10	11	12
0	0	0	0	0	0	0	0	0	0	0	0	0	0
1	0	1	2	3	4	5	6	7	8	9	10	11	12
2	0	2	4	6	8	10	12	14	16	18	20	22	24
3	0	3	6	9	12	15	18	21	24	27	30	33	36
4	0	4	8	12	16	20	24	28	32	36	40	44	48
5	0	5	10	15	20	25	30	35	40	45	50	55	60
6	0	6	12	18	24	30	36	42	48	54	60	66	72
7	0	7	14	21	28	35	42	49	56	63	70	77	84
8	0	8	16	24	32	40	48	56	64	72	80	88	96
9	0	9	18	27	36	45	54	63	72	81	90	99	108
10	0	10	20	30	40	50	60	70	80	90	100	110	120
11	0	11	22	33	44	55	66	77	88	99	110	121	132
12	0	12	24	36	48	60	72	84	96	108	120	132	144

How Much Does Lunch Cost?

Level: Emerging

Skills: Listening, Speaking, Reading

Objective: Answer questions about how much lunch costs

Materials: food/price chart

Activity Give students a chart that lists the price of some lunch items.

Point to a picture or name a food item. Ask the questions and model the language children should use to answer the questions. Then have students repeat the answers.

Students at the Emerging level may have difficulty answering the questions in a complete sentence, so allow them to respond with just the price as they gain confidence and skill.

Students can also be asked about the price of several food items (**How much do three hot dogs cost? They cost $6**) or about the combined price of food items (**How much does a slice of pizza and a milk cost? They cost $2.10**).

Leveling: Expanding Have students take turns asking and answering the questions. Write the sentence frames for students to work independently.

STRATEGY
Model Language

How Tall? How Old?

Level: Expanding

Skills: Listening, Speaking, Reading

Objective: Ask and answer questions about height and age

Materials: tape measure, index cards, pencil

Activity Place a tape measure (in customary units) on the wall and have group members measure each other's height.

Have each student write his or her name, age, and height (in feet and inches) on an index card.

The students place the index cards face up on the table. Students take turns asking questions about the age and height of other students.

How tall is __Juana__ ?
__She__ is __4 feet 5 inches__ tall.

How old is __Peter__ ?
__He__ is __ten__ years old.

Make sure students use the correct pronoun in each answer.

Extension Encourage students to ask comparative questions. For example, **Who is older, Juana or Peter?**

Leveling: Emerging Read and model the question and answer. Students will repeat the answer.

Students at the Emerging level may have difficulty answering the question in a complete sentence, so allow them to respond with just the height or age as they gain confidence and skill.

How Much? How Many?

Level: Expanding
Skills: Listening, Speaking, Reading
Objective: Answer questions about money
Materials: play coins or bills, paper, pencil

Activity Give students a collection of coins or bills. One student chooses a handful of coins and keeps them hidden from the other student. The partner asks the following questions and writes down the answers.

How many quarters do you have?
How many dimes do you have?
How many nickels do you have?
How many pennies do you have?

Write the sentence frames and have the first student ask questions about their coins.

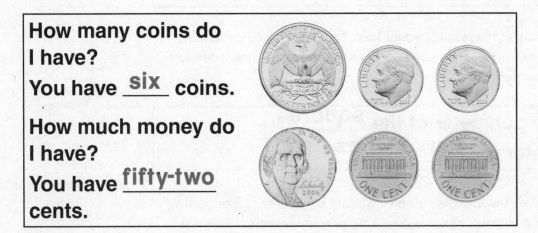

How many coins do I have?
You have ___six___ coins.
How much money do I have?
You have __fifty-two__ cents.

The partner answers these questions based on the information gathered. Then, the first student shows the coins and checks the answers.

This activity can also be performed with bills or a mixture of coins and bills.

Extension Have students ask more questions about the coins, such as, **If you give me 35 cents more, how much money would I have?**

Leveling: Emerging Read and model each question and answer. Students will repeat the answers.

STRATEGY
Model Language

Distance and Perimeter

Level: Expanding

Skills: Listening, Speaking, Reading

Objective: Answer questions about distance and perimeter

Materials: classroom objects, pictures of rectangles, ruler, meter stick, yard stick, paper, pencil

Activity Have students practice describing distance. Select two objects in the classroom. Write the sentence frames and have students ask, measure, and then answer the question about distance. Students can round to the nearest unit or make a more precise measurement using units of measure they are studying.

> **What is the distance between __the door__ and __your desk__?**
>
> **The distance is __five__ __feet__.**

Give students pictures of rectangles and have them describe perimeter. Write the sentence frames and have students ask, measure, and answer the question about perimeter.

> **What is the perimeter of the __square__?**
> **The perimeter is __ten__ __inches__.**

Extension Have students discuss how finding perimeter is like finding distance. Ask them to think of a way to define perimeter using the word "distance." **Perimeter is the distance around something.**

Leveling: Emerging Read and model the question and answer. Students will repeat the answer.

Students at the Emerging level may have difficulty answering the question in a complete sentence, so allow them to respond with just the distance or perimeter as they gain confidence and skill.

Compare Two Shapes

Level: Expanding
Skills: Speaking, Reading, Writing
Objective: Compare shapes by adding -er to the adjective.
Materials: paper, pencil, ruler

Activity Select 5 shapes or geometric figures for partners to draw. Then have students look at each other's papers and take turns comparing their figures by completing the sentence frames.

Students should both say and write their comparative sentences.

My _____ **is** _____. figure adjective **Your** _____ **is** same figure _____. adjective with -er **Adjective word bank:** tall long short small wide big narrow large	**For example:** **My rectangle is wide.** **Your rectangle is wider.**

Make sure students' comparative sentences are true based on the pictures they draw. Also, check the spelling of the comparative adjectives, specifically for "wider," "bigger," and "larger."

Extension Display all students' papers at the front of the room. Have students take turns comparing 2 shapes or figures. For example, **Marc's line is shorter than Jeannette's line,** or **Jeannette's line is short, but Marc's line is shorter.**

Leveling: Emerging Draw two of each shape or figure on the board, and write the sentence frames as well as the word bank. Point to a figure and read the first sentence, for example, **This square is small.** Then have the students point and reply chorally, **That square is smaller.**

STRATEGY
Model
Language

Compare Three Shapes

Level: Expanding

Skills: Speaking, Reading, Writing

Objective: Compare shapes by using -er and -est

Materials: paper, pencil

Activity Place students in groups of three. Write the sentence frames and adjective word bank for students.

My _____ is _____.
   figure   adjective

My _____ is _____.
  same figure   adjective with -er

My _____ is _____.
  same figure   adjective with -est

Adjective word bank:

tall	long	short	small
wide	big	narrow	large

The first student draws a shape or geometric figure and makes a statement about the figure. For example, **My circle is small.** The second student draws a smaller figure and says, **My circle is smaller.** The third student draws an even smaller figure and says, **My circle is smallest.**

Have the students switch roles and repeat the activity for several more shapes or figures.

Extension Have students write summary sentences based on the activity. For example, **Simon's circle is small. Alicia's circle is smaller. Phillip's circle is smallest.** Students can take turns reading their sentences to the group.

Leveling: Emerging Three students can draw figures on the board, and the teacher can model the sentences. **Simon's circle is small. Alicia's circle is smaller. Phillip's circle is smallest.** Students repeat the sentences.

STRATEGY
Model
Language

Stick Figure Spelling

Level: Bridging

Skills: Reading, Writing

Objective: Practice recalling and spelling math words

Materials: 6–10 words, use the vocabulary charts, pages 61–85, or vocabulary from the chapter; paper; pencil

Activity Play a sample game with students to explain the rules. Choose a math word for them to guess, and draw blank spaces for each letter in the word.

Students take turns guessing a letter in the word. If the letter is in the word, write it in the correct space. If it is not in the word, draw one part of a stick figure.

Students try to guess the word before the stick figure is complete. Keep track of the letters that don't belong in the word so that none are repeated.

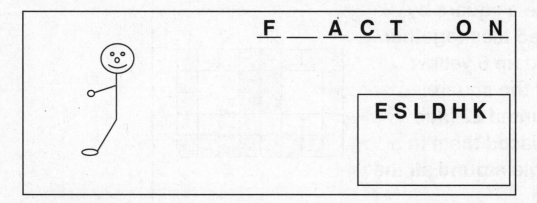

After modeling a game, have students play with a partner to practice the math vocabulary they are studying.

Extension When a student figures out the word, he or she must give the correct definition in order to win. The partner to win three games is the champion.

Leveling: Expanding Provide a limited word list to choose from or allow only current or recently-studied vocabulary.

How Did You Build It?

Level: Bridging

Skills: Listening, Speaking, Reading, Writing

Objective: Describe an arrangement of tiles or pattern blocks

Materials: color tiles or pattern blocks, paper, pencil

Activity Give students color tiles or pattern blocks. Have partners sit so they can't see each other's workspace.

Have the first student make a simple arrangement of tiles or pattern blocks, and then describe in detail how he or she made it. As the student describes it, the partner tries to build it the same way.

When they are finished, the second partner repeats the directions for making the arrangement. Then the partners compare the arrangements and switch roles.

First I made a square by putting 4 red tiles together. Next, I lined up 6 yellow tiles under the square. Then, I counted 22 blue tiles and placed them in a big rectangle around all the other tiles.

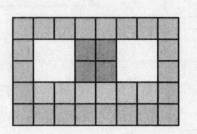

Extension Have students write the directions for making another tile or pattern block arrangement. Have the partners trade papers and then make the arrangement from the written directions. Partners then rewrite the directions, using the original directions as a model.

Leveling: Expanding Read a description of a pattern to partners. Have the students make the pattern that is described. Give them a written description with key words missing and have them fill in the missing words.

STRATEGY
Model Language

Compare and Contrast

Level: Bridging

Skills: Speaking, Reading, Writing

Objective: Compare and contrast two math concepts

Materials: paper, pencil

Activity Have partners write sentences to compare and contrast two math concepts. Have students write the sentence frames and fill in the blanks with the appropriate words to compare the concepts.

Students can compare shapes, properties, translations, fractions, or any other math concepts they are studying. For example,

---

Compare a square ▢ and a triangle ◺.

1. __A square__ and __a triangle__ are different in that __squares__ is/are/has/have __4 angles__, but __triangles__ is/are/has/have __3 angles__.

2. While __squares__ and __triangles__ are both __polygons__, there are several differences between them. The most important is that __squares__ is/are/has/have __4 sides__ and __triangles__ is/are/has/have __3 sides__.

3. __Squares__ is/are/has/have __equilateral__, but __not all triangles__ is/are/has/have __equilateral__.

Extension Have students work on their own to compare two math concepts without using the sentence frames. Partners should write their paragraphs on separate sheets of paper and then compare paragraphs when they are done.

Leveling: Expanding Provide a word bank for completing the sentences.

STRATEGY
Model Language

Write an Explanation

Level: Bridging

Skills: Reading, Writing

Objective: Write a paragraph to explain a math topic

Materials: paper, pencil

Activity Give partners a math question to answer in a paragraph. They should explain their reasoning in short, concise sentences. They should also include an example and end with a conclusion.

Sample questions:

- Are all squares rectangles? Are all rectangles squares?
- Why are all multiples of 6 divisible by 3 and 2?
- Why does the Commutative Property not work with subtraction and division?
- Why do you need a common denominator when you add fractions?

Sample explanation for the first pair of questions:

A rectangle is a shape with 4 sides and 4 right angles. It also has 2 pairs of equal sides. All squares have 4 sides, 4 right angles, and 2 pairs of equal sides, so all squares must be rectangles. A square is a shape that has 4 equal sides and 4 right angles. Not all rectangles have 4 equal sides, so not all rectangles are squares. In conclusion, we can say that all squares are rectangles but not all rectangles are squares.

Extension Have students read their explanations to another group for clarity and to receive feedback.

Leveling: Expanding Provide a word bank and a sample explanation with key words removed. Have students fill in the words that complete the explanation. Students read their explanations aloud.

PLACE VALUE VOCABULARY

Use the EL definitions with students to help them understand math terms related to place value. The terms are organized by grade level so teachers can find vocabulary that applies to their students. For grade 4, students should also use grade 3 vocabulary. For grade 5, students should also use grade 3 and grade 4 vocabulary. For grade 6, students should use grade 3, grade 4, and grade 5 vocabulary.

Grade	English	Spanish Cognate	Definition
3	digits	digitos	Digits are the symbols 0, 1, 2, 3, 4, 5, 6, 7, 8, and 9. They can have different place values, depending where they are in a number.
3	expanded form		Expanded form is a way to write numbers. It shows the value of each digit. The expanded form of 768 is 700 + 60 + 8.
3	place value		Place value is the value of a digit in a number. This value is based on the location of the digit in the number.
3	standard form		Standard form is a way to write numbers. It uses the digits 0–9. Each digit has a place value. In the number 16, 1 has the value of 10 and 6 has the value of 6.
3	word form		Word form is a way to write a number in words. The word form of 92 is ninety-two.
4	millions	millones	Millions is the period after thousands.
4	period	período	In a multidigit number, a period is each group of three digits separated by commas.

Teacher's Tips

In some Spanish-speaking countries, the symbols separating digits to indicate place value (the comma and the decimal point) are used in an opposite way than they are in the United States. For example, 4.670 = four thousand six hundred seventy; 0,2 = two tenths.

NUMBERS & OPERATIONS VOCABULARY

Use the EL definitions with students to help them understand math terms related to numbers and operations. The terms are organized by grade level so teachers can find vocabulary that applies to their students. For grade 4, students should also use grade 3 vocabulary. For grade 5, students should also use grade 3 and grade 4 vocabulary. For grade 6, students should use grade 3, grade 4, and grade 5 vocabulary.

Grade	English	Spanish Cognate	Definition
3	addend		An addend is any of the numbers that are added in addition.
3	addition		Addition is a process. In this process you find the total number of items when two or more groups of items are joined. It is the opposite operation of subtraction.
3	array		An array is a set of objects or numbers. An array is arranged in rows and columns.
3	Associative Property (of Addition)	propiedad asociativa (de la suma)	This property states that you can group addends in different ways and still get the same sum.
3	Associative Property (of Multiplication)	propiedad asociativa (de la multiplicación)	This property states that you can change the grouping of factors and still get the same product.
3	benchmark numbers		Benchmark numbers are numbers that are easy to work with in mental math. 1/2 and 1 are benchmark numbers.
3	cent sign (¢)		The cent sign is used to show money amounts less than one dollar. 53 cents is written 53¢.
3	change		Change is the money you get back if you have paid for an item with coins or bills that have a value greater than the cost of the item.
3	Commutative Property (of Addition)	propiedad conmutativa (de la suma)	This property states that the order in which you add two or more numbers does not change the sum.
3	Commutative Property (of Multiplication)	propiedad conmutativa (de la multiplicación)	This property states that you can multiply two factors in any order and get the same product.

Teacher's Tips

The terms for multiplication properties (Identity Property, Commutative Property, Associative Property) look like the terms for addition properties. Provide an example to help students gain understanding of the definitions and remember the differences.

Grade	English	Spanish Cognate	Definition
3	compare	comparar	To compare is to find whether numbers are equal to, less than, or greater than each other.
3	compatible numbers	números compatibles	Compatible numbers are numbers that are easy to compute with mentally. Compatible numbers are often used in mental math.
3	difference	diferencia	The difference is the answer in a subtraction problem.
3	dime		A dime is a coin worth 10 cents (10¢). A dime is equal to 10 pennies.
3	Distributive Property (of Multiplication)	propiedad distributive (de la multiplicación)	This property states that multiplying a sum by a number is the same as multiplying each addend by the number and then adding the products.
3	divide	dividir	To divide is to separate an amount into smaller, equal groups. It is the opposite operation of multiplication.
3	dividend	dividendo	In a division problem, the dividend is the number that is to be divided. In $35 \div 5 = 7$, 35 is the dividend.
3	division	división	Division is an operation. It is the process of sharing a number of items to find how many groups can be made or how many items will be in a group. Division is the opposite operation of multiplication.
3	divisor	divisor	In a division problem, the divisor is the number that divides the dividend. The divisor stands for the number of groups or for how many in each group. In $35 \div 5 = 7$, 5 is the divisor.
3	dollar	dólar	A dollar is paper money worth 100 cents. A dollar is equal to 100 pennies. It is written as $1.00.
3	equal groups	grupos iguales	Equal groups have the same number of objects.
3	equal sign (=)	signo de iugaldad	The equal sign is a symbol. It is used to show that two numbers have the same value.
3	equal to (=)	igual a	The phrase *equal to* means "having the same value."
3	equivalent	equivalente	Two or more sets that are equivalent name the same amount.

Teacher's Tips

Terms like *difference/diferencia* and *dividend/dividendo* are cognates. If students are familiar with the Spanish term, help them relate it to the English term by pointing out similarities and differences between the Spanish word and the English word.

63

Grade	English	Spanish Cognate	Definition
3	estimate (v.)	estimar	To estimate is to find about how many or about how much.
3	estimate (n.)	estimación	An estimate is a number that is close to an exact amount. An estimate tells about how much or about how many.
3	even		An even number is a whole number. It has 0, 2, 4, 6, or 8 in the ones place.
3	fact family		A fact family is a set of related equations. One kind of fact family is a set of related multiplication and division equations. Another kind of fact family is a set of related addition and subtraction equations.
3	factors	factores	Factors are the numbers you multiply to find a product. In the multiplication problem $2 \times 5 = 10$, the factors are 2 and 5.
3	greater than (>)		The symbol that means "greater than" is used to compare two numbers. The greater number is given first.
3	half dollar		A half dollar is a coin worth 50 cents (50¢). A half dollar is equal to 50 pennies.
3	Identity Property (of Addition)	propiedad de identidad (de la suma)	This property states that when you add zero to a number, the result is that number.
3	Identity Property (of Multiplication)	propiedad de identidad (de la multiplicación)	This property states that the product of any number and 1 is that number.
3	inverse operations	operaciones inversas	Inverse operations are operations that undo each other. Addition and subtraction are inverse operations. Multiplication and division are inverse operations.
3	less than (<)		The symbol that means "less than" is used to compare two numbers. The lesser number is given first.
3	multiple	múltiplo	A multiple is a number that is the product of two counting numbers.

Grade	English	Spanish Cognate	Definition
3	multiplication	multiplicación	Multiplication is an operation. When you multiply, you find the total number of items in two or more equal groups. Multiplication is the opposite operation of division.
3	multiply	multiplicar	To multiply is to combine equal groups. You multiply to find how many in all. The opposite of multiplication is division.
3	nickel		A nickel is a coin worth 5 cents (5¢). A nickel is equal to 5 pennies.
3	number line		A number line is a line on which numbers can be located.
3	odd		An odd number is a whole number. It has 1, 3, 5, 7, or 9 in the ones place.
3	product	producto	The product is the answer in a multiplication problem.
3	quarter		A quarter is a coin worth 25 cents (25¢). A quarter is equal to 25 pennies.
3	quotient	cociente	The quotient is the number, not including the remainder, that results from division. In 35 ÷ 5 = 7, 7 is the quotient.
3	regroup	reagrupar	To regroup is a way of renaming a number. To regroup, use place value to exchange equal amounts.
3	remainder		The remainder is the amount left over when a number cannot be divided evenly.
3	round		To round is to replace a number with another number that tells about how many or about how much. Round to the nearest 10, 100, 1,000, and so on.
3	subtraction		Subtraction is an operation. When you subtract, you find how many are left when a number of items are taken away from a group of items. Subtraction is also the process of finding the difference when two groups are compared. It is the opposite operation of addition.
3	sum	suma	The sum is the answer to an addition problem.

Teacher's Tips

Many number and operations concepts are best demonstrated with examples and drawings. Provide examples and illustrations whenever possible to help students gain understanding of the definitions.

Grade	English	Spanish Cognate	Definition
3	whole number		A whole number is one of the numbers 0, 1, 2, 3, 4, …. The set of whole numbers goes on without end.
3	Zero Property (of multiplication)	propiedad del cero (de la multiplicación)	The Zero Property states that the product of zero and any number is zero.
4	common factor	factor común	A common factor is a number that is a factor of two or more numbers.
4	doubles	dobles	Doubles have two addends. Both addends are the same number.
4	front-end estimation		Front-end estimation is a method of estimating sums or differences. This method uses the front digits of the numbers.
4	greater than or equal to (≥)		The symbol that means "greater than or equal to" is used to compare two quantities. The first quantity is greater than or equal to the second quantity.
4	less than or equal to (≤)		The symbol that means "less than or equal to" is used to compare two quantities. The first quantity is less than or equal to the second quantity.
4	million	millón	A million is a counting number. It is the number after 999,999. It is the same as 1,000 thousands. It is written as 1,000,000.
4	not equal to (≠)	no igual a	This symbol indicates that one quantity is not equal to another quantity.
4	numerical expression	expresión numérica	A numerical expression is a mathematical phrase. It uses only numbers and operation signs.
4	partial product	producto parcial	The partial product is a method of multiplying. Ones, tens, hundreds, and so on are multiplied separately. Then the products are added together.
4	percent	por ciento	Percent is the comparison of a number to 100. The word *percent* means "per hundred."

Grade	English	Spanish Cognate	Definition
4	square number		A square number is a product. The factors are the number and itself.
5	base (of a power)	base	A base is a number used as a repeated factor.
5	billion		A billion is a counting number. It is the same as 1,000 millions. It is written as 1,000,000,000.
5	composite number	número compuesto	A composite number has more than two factors.
5	divisible	divisible	A number is divisible by another number if the quotient is a counting number and the remainder is zero.
5	exponent	exponente	An exponent is the number that shows how many times the base is used as the factor.
5	factor tree		A factor tree is a diagram. It shows the prime factors of a number.
5	greatest common factor (GCF)		The greatest common factor is the greatest factor that two or more numbers have in common.
5	integers	enteros	Integers are the set of whole numbers and their opposites.
5	ladder diagram		A ladder diagram is a kind of diagram. It shows the steps of repeated division. Division is repeated by a prime number until the quotient is reached.
5	least common multiple (LCM)		The least common multiple is the least number, other than zero, that is a common multiple of two or more numbers.
5	negative integer	entero negativo	A negative integer is any integer less than zero.
5	opposites	opuestos	Opposite numbers are two numbers that are the same distance from zero on a number line. The numbers are the same distance in opposite directions.
5	overestimate		An overstimate is an estimate that is greater than the exact answer.

Grade	English	Spanish Cognate	Definition
5	partial quotient	cociente parcial	The partial quotient is a method of dividing. To get the partial quotient, multiples of the divisor are divided separately. Then the quotients are added together.
5	perfect square		A perfect square is a number. It is the product of a number and itself.
5	positive integer	entero positivo	A positive integer is any integer greater than zero.
5	prime factor	factor primo	A prime factor is a factor that is a prime number.
5	prime factorization		Prime factorization is a way to show a number. The number is written as the product of all its prime factors.
5	prime number	número primo	A prime number has exactly two factors: 1 and itself.
5	underestimate		An understimate is an estimate that is less than the exact answer.

FRACTIONS & DECIMALS VOCABULARY

Use the EL definitions with students to help them understand math terms related to fractions and decimals. The terms are organized by grade level so teachers can find vocabulary that applies to their students. For grade 4, students should also use grade 3 vocabulary. For grade 5, students should also use grade 3 and grade 4 vocabulary. For grade 6, students should use grade 3, grade 4, and grade 5 vocabulary.

Grade	English	Spanish Cognate	Definition
3	denominator	denominador	The denominator is the part of a fraction below the line. The denominator tells the total number of equal parts of the whole or the group.
3	eighths		An eighth is a fraction. Something divided into eighths is divided into eight equal parts.
3	equal parts	partes iguales	Equal parts are parts of a whole that are exactly the same size.
3	equivalent fractions	fracciones equivalentes	Equivalent fractions are two or more fractions that name the same amount.
3	fifths		A fifth is a fraction. Something divided into fifths is divided into five equal parts.
3	fourths		A fourth is a fraction. Something divided into fourths is divided into four equal parts.
3	fraction	fracción	A fraction is a number that names part of a whole or part of a group.
3	halves		Halves are a kind of equal part. Something divided into halves is divided into two equal parts.
3	like fractions		Like fractions have the same denominator.
3	mixed number	número mixto	A mixed number contains a whole number and a fraction part.
3	numerator	numerador	The numerator is the part of a fraction above the line. The numerator tells how many equal parts of the whole are being counted.
3	order	ordenar	To order numbers is to arrange them in a certain way. One way to order numbers is from least to greatest.
3	sixths		A sixth is a fraction. Something divided into sixths is divided into six equal parts.
3	tenths		A tenth is a fraction. Something divided into tenths is divided into ten equal parts.

Teacher's Tips

Be aware that English language learners may have difficulty distinguishing the difference in sound and spelling of words such as *tens* and *tenths*.

Grade	English	Spanish Cognate	Definition
3	thirds		A third is a fraction. Something divided into thirds is divided into three equal parts.
3	twelfths		A twelfth is a fraction. Something divided into twelfths is divided into twelve equal parts.
3	unit fraction	fracción unitaria	A unit fraction has 1 as its numerator.
3	unlike fractions		Unlike fractions are fractions that have different denominators.
4	common denominator	denominador común	A common denominator is the same number used as a denominator in two or more fractions.
4	common multiple	múltiplo común	A common multiple is a multiple of two or more numbers.
4	decimal	decimal	A decimal is a number. It has one or more digits to the right of the decimal point.
4	decimal point	punto decimal	A decimal point is a symbol used to separate the ones and the tenths places in a decimal.
4	equivalent decimals	decimales equivalentes	Equivalent decimals are two or more decimals that name the same amount.
4	hundredth		A hundredth is a fraction. It stands for one of one hundred equal parts of a whole.
4	simplest form		A fraction is in its simplest form when 1 is the only number that can divide evenly into the numerator and the denominator.
4	thousandth		A thousandth is a decimal or fraction. It stands for one of one thousand equal parts.
5	decimal system	sistema decimal	The decimal system is a system of computation. It is based on the number 10.
5	greatest common factor (GCF)		This is the greatest common factor of two or more numbers.
5	least common denominator (LCD)		This is the least common multiple of two or more denominators.

Teacher's Tips

Be aware that English language learners may have difficulty distinguishing the difference in sound and spelling of words such as *hundreds* and *hundredths.*

The terms *least common denominator* (LCD) and *least common multiple* (LCM) are similar in sound, spelling, and appearance, which some students might find confusing.

MEASUREMENT VOCABULARY

Use the EL definitions with students to help them understand math terms related to measurement. The terms are organized by grade level so teachers can find vocabulary that applies to their students. For grade 4, students should also use grade 3 vocabulary. For grade 5, students should also use grade 3 and grade 4 vocabulary. For grade 6, students should use grade 3, grade 4, and grade 5 vocabulary.

Grade	English	Spanish Cognate	Definition
3	A.M.	a.m.	A.M. stands for the hours between midnight and noon.
3	analog clock		An analog clock is a tool for measuring time. Its hands move around a circle. The circle has numbers. The clock hands show the hours, minutes, and sometimes seconds.
3	calendar	calendario	A calendar is a chart. It shows the days, weeks, and months of a year.
3	capacity	capacidad	The capacity of a container is the amount it can hold when it is full.
3	centimeter (cm)	centímetro (cm)	A centimeter is a metric unit of measurement. It is used to measure length or distance.
3	cup (c)		A cup is a customary unit of measurement. It is used to measure capacity.
3	decimeter (dm)	decímetro (dm)	A decimeter is a metric unit of measurement. It is used to measure length or distance.
3	digital clock		A digital clock is an instrument that tells time. It shows time to the minute. It uses digits to show the time.
3	elapsed time		Elapsed time is the time that passes from the start of an activity until the end of that activity.
3	foot (ft)		A foot is a customary unit of measurement. It is used to measure length or distance. 1 foot equals 12 inches.
3	gallon (gal)	galón (gal)	A gallon is a customary unit of measurement. It is used to measure capacity. 1 gallon equals 4 quarts.
3	gram (g)	gramo (g)	A gram is a metric unit of measurement. It is used to measure mass.
3	half hour		A half hour is 30 minutes.
3	hour (hr)	hora (h)	An hour is a unit used to measure time. 1 hour equals 60 minutes

Teacher's Tips

Terms like *centimeter/centímetro*, *decimeter/decímetro*, *liter/litro*, and *mass/masa* are cognates. If students are familiar with the Spanish term, help them relate it to the English term by pointing out similarities and differences between the Spanish word and the English word.

Grade	English	Spanish Cognate	Definition
3	hour hand		The hour hand is found on an analog clock. It is the shorter hand.
3	inch (in.)		An inch is a customary unit of measurement. It is used to measure length or distance.
3	kilogram (kg)	kilogramo (kg)	A kilogram is a metric unit of measurement. It is used to measure mass. 1 kilogram equals 1,000 grams.
3	kilometer (km)	kilómetro (km)	A kilometer is a metric unit of measurement. It is used to measure length or distance. 1 kilometer equals 1,000 meters
3	length		Length is a measurement. It is the distance between two points.
3	liter (L)	litro (L)	A liter is a metric unit of measurement. It is used to measure capacity. 1 liter equals 1,000 milliliters.
3	mass	masa	Mass is a measurement of the amount of matter in an object. It is often measured in grams or kilograms.
3	meter (m)	metro (m)	A meter is a metric unit of measurement. It is used to measure length or distance. 1 meter equals 100 centimeters.
3	midnight		Midnight is a time of day. Midnight is 12:00 at night.
3	mile (mi)	milla (mi)	A mile is a customary unit of measurement. It is used to measure length or distance. 5,280 feet equal 1 mile.
3	milliliter (mL)	mililitro (mL)	A milliliter is a metric unit of measurement. It is used to measure capacity. 1,000 milliliters equal 1 liter.
3	minute (min)	minuto (min)	A minute is a unit used to measure short amounts of time. There are 60 minutes in 1 hour.
3	minute hand		The minute hand is found on an analog clock. It is the longer hand.
3	noon		Noon is a time of day. Noon is 12:00 during the day.
3	ounce (oz)	onza (oz)	An ounce is a customary unit of measurement. It is used to measure weight. 16 ounces equal 1 pound.
3	perimeter	perímetro	The perimiter is the distance around a plane figure.
3	pint (pt)	pinta (pt)	A pint is a customary unit of measurement. It is used to measure capacity. 1 pint equals 2 cups.
3	P.M.		P.M. stands for the hours between noon and midnight.

Grade	English	Spanish Cognate	Definition
3	pound (lb)		A pound is a customary unit of measurement. It is used to measure weight. 1 pound equals 16 ounces.
3	quart (qt)	cuarto (ct)	A quart is a customary unit of measurement. It is used to measure capacity. 1 quart equals 2 pints.
3	quarter hour	cuarto de hora	A quarter hour is 15 minutes.
3	second (sec)	segundo (s)	A second is a small unit of time. 1 minute equals 60 seconds.
3	weight		Weight is how heavy an object is.
3	yard (yd)	yarda (yd)	A yard is a customary unit of measurement. It is used to measure length or distance. 1 yard equals 3 feet.
4	area	área	The area is the number of square units needed to cover a flat surface.
4	clockwise		Clockwise is a direction. It is the direction in which the hands of a clock move.
4	counterclockwise		Counterclockwise is a direction. It is the opposite direction in which the hands of a clock move.
4	degree (°)		A degree is a unit of measurement. It is used to measure angles. It is also used to measure temperature.
4	grid		A grid is made up of evenly-divided and equally-spaced squares. These squares are on a shape or flat surface.
4	half square unit		A half square unit is half of a unit of area.
4	height		Height is a kind of measurement. It is the length of a perpendicular from the base to the top of a plane shape or a solid shape.
4	linear units	unidades lineales	Linear units are units of measurement. They measure length, width, height, or distance.
4	millimeter (mm)	milímetro (mm)	A millimeter is metric unit of measurement. It is used to measure length or distance. 1 centimeter equals 10 millimeters.
4	one-dimensional	unidimensional	A one-dimensional measure is a measure in only one direction. Length is a one-dimensional measure.
4	protractor		A protractor is a measuring tool. It is used to measure the size of an angle.

Teacher's Tips

The words *yard* and *pound* have multiple meanings. Find out what students think each term means. When possible, relate the precise math meaning to one that students already know.

Grade	English	Spanish Cognate	Definition
4	square unit		A square unit is a unit of area. It has dimensions of 1 unit × 1 unit.
5	balance	balancear	To balance is to make equal in weight or in number.
5	Celsius (C)	Celsius (C)	Celsius is a metric scale of measurement. It is used to measure temperature.
5	cubic unit	unidad cúbica	A cubic unit is a unit of volume. It has dimensions of 1 unit × 1 unit × 1 unit.
5	degree Celsius (°C)		A degree Celsius is a metric unit of measurement. It is used to measure temperature.
5	degree Fahrenheit (°F)		A degree Fahrenheit is a customary unit of measurement. It is used to measure temperature.
5	dekameter (dam)	decámetro (dam)	A dekameter is a metric unit of measurement. It is a measure of length or distance. 1 dekameter equals 10 meters.
5	Fahrenheit (F)	Fahrenheit (F)	Fahrenheit is a customary scale of measurement. It is used to measure temperature.
5	fluid ounce (fl oz)	onza fluida (oz fl)	A fluid ounce is a customary unit of measurement. It is used to measure capacity. 8 fluid ounces equal 1 cup.
5	milligram (mg)	miligramo (mg)	A milligram is a metric unit of measurement. It is used to measure mass. 1 gram equals 1,000 milligrams.
5	pan balance		A pan balance is an instrument used to compare the weights of objects.
5	precision	precisión	Precision is a property of measurement. The smaller the unit of measure used, the more precise the measurement is.
5	surface area		Surface area is the sum of the areas of all the faces, or surfaces, of a solid figure
5	tablespoon (tbsp)		A tablespoon is a customary unit of measurement. It is used to measure capacity. 1 tablespoon equals 3 teaspoons.
5	teaspoon (tsp)		A teaspoon is a customary unit of measurement. It is used to measure capacity. 3 teaspoons equal 1 tablespoon.
5	ton (T)	tonelada (t)	A ton is a customary unit of measurement. It is used to measure weight. 1 ton equals 2,000 pounds.
5	volume	volumen	Volume is the measure of the space a solid figure occupies. Volume is measured in cubic units.

GEOMETRY VOCABULARY

Use the EL definitions with students to help them understand math terms related to geometry. The terms are organized by grade level so teachers can find vocabulary that applies to their students. For grade 4, students should also use grade 3 vocabulary. For grade 5, students should also use grade 3 and grade 4 vocabulary. For grade 6, students should use grade 3, grade 4, and grade 5 vocabulary.

Grade	English	Spanish Cognate	Definition
3	acute angle	ángulo agudo	An acute angle has a measure less than a right angle (greater than 0° and less than 90°).
3	acute triangle	triángulo acutángulo	An acute triangle is a triangle that has three acute angles.
3	angle	ángulo	An angle is formed by two rays that share an endpoint.
3	circle	círculo	A circle is a closed plane shape. It has a round shape.
3	closed shape		A closed shape begins and ends at the same point. It can have any shape.
3	cone	cono	A cone is a solid, pointed figure. It has a flat, round base.
3	congruent	congruente	Shapes that are congruent have the same size and shape.
3	cube	cubo	A cube is a solid figure with six congruent square faces.
3	cylinder	cilindro	A cylinder is a solid or hollow object. It is shaped like a can.
3	decagon	decágono	A decagon is a polygon. It has ten sides and ten angles.
3	diagonal	diagonal	A diagonal is a line segment. It connects two vertices of a polygon that are not next to each other.
3	equilateral triangle	triángulo equilátero	An equilateral triangle has three equal sides and three equal angles.

Teacher's Tips

Terms like *cone/cono*, *congruent/congruente*, *symmetry/simetría*, and *vertex/vértice* are cognates. If students are familiar with the Spanish term, help them relate it to the English term by pointing out similarities and differences between the Spanish word and the English word.

Grade	English	Spanish Cognate	Definition
3	hexagon	hexágono	A hexagon is a polygon. It has six sides and six angles.
3	intersecting (lines)	líneas intersecantes	Lines that intersect are lines that meet or cross each other.
3	isosceles triangle	triángulo isósceles	An isosceles triangle has two equal sides.
3	line	línea	A line is a straight path. It extends in both directions. A line has no endpoints.
3	line of symmetry	línea de simetría	A line of symmetry is an imaginary line on a shape. If the shape were folded on this line, the two parts would match exactly.
3	line segment	segmento	A line segment is part of a line. It includes two points, called endpoints, and all of the points between them.
3	obtuse angle	ángulo obtuso	An obtuse angle has a measure greater than 90° and less than 180°.
3	obtuse triangle	triángulo obtusángulo	An obtuse triangle has one obtuse angle.
3	octagon	octágono	An octagon is a polygon. It has eight sides and eight angles.
3	open shape		An open shape does not begin and end at the same point. It can have any shape.
3	parallel (lines)	líneas paralelas	Parallel lines never cross and are always the same distance apart.
3	parallelogram	paralelogramo	A parallelogram is a quadrilateral with two pairs of parallel sides and two pairs of sides of equal length.
3	pentagon	pentágono	A pentagon is a polygon. It has five sides and five angles.
3	perpendicular lines	líneas perpendiculares	Perpendicular lines intersect. When they intersect, they form a right angle.
3	plane shape		A plane shape is a shape in a plane. A plane shape is formed by curves, line segments, or curves and line segments.
3	point	punto	A point is an exact position or location.
3	polygon	polígono	A polygon is a closed plane shape. It has straight sides that are line segments.

Grade	English	Spanish Cognate	Definition
3	quadrilateral	cuadrilátero	A quadrilaterial is a polygon. It has four sides and four angles.
3	ray	rayo	A ray is part of a line. It has one endpoint. It goes on without end in one direction.
3	rectangle	rectángulo	A rectangle is a quadrilateral. It has two pairs of parallel sides. It has two pairs of equal sides. It has four right angles.
3	rectangular prism	prisma rectangular	A rectangular prism is a solid shape. It has six faces. Each face is a rectangle.
3	regular polygon	polígono regular	A regular polygon is a polygon whose sides are equal in length. All its angles are equal in measure.
3	rhombus	rombo	A rhombus is a quadrilateral. It has two pairs of parallel sides. It has four equal sides and four angles.
3	right angle		A right angle is an angle that forms a square corner.
3	right triangle	triángulo rectángulo	A right triangle has one right angle.
3	scalene triangle	triángulo escaleno	A scalene triangle has no equal sides.
3	side		A side is a straight line segment in a polygon.
3	sphere	esfera	A sphere is a solid shape. It has the shape of a round ball.
3	square		A square is a quadrilateral. It has two pairs of parallel sides. It has four sides of equal length. It has four right angles.
3	square pyramid		A square pyramid is a solid, pointed shape. It has a flat base. The base is square.
3	straight angle		In a straight angle, the two rays point in opposite directions. They form a line. A straight angle is an angle with a measure of 180°.
3	symmetry	simetría	A shape has symmetry if it can be folded along a line so that the two parts match exactly. One half of the shape looks like the mirror image of the other half.
3	three-dimensional shape		A three-dimensional shape has length, width, and height.
3	trapezoid	trapecio	A trapezoid is a quadrilateral. It has exactly one pair of parallel sides. It has four angles.

Grade	English	Spanish Cognate	Definition
3	triangle	triángulo	A triangle is a polygon. It has three sides and three angles.
3	two-dimensional shape		A two-dimensional shape has length and width.
3	vertex/vertices	vértice/vértices	The vertex is the point at which two rays of an angle or two (or more) line segments meet. The vertex is also where three or more edges meet in a three-dimensional shape.
4	base	base	For a two-dimensional shape, the base is one side of a triangle or parallelogram which is used to help find the area. For a three-dimensional shape, the base is a plane figure. It is usually a polygon or circle. It is used to help find the volume of some solid figures.
4	center	centro	The center is a point inside a circle. It is the same distance from each point on the circle.
4	corner		The corner is the point on a plane shape where two line segments meet.
4	dimension	dimensión	A dimension is a measure in one direction, such as length.
4	endpoint		An endpoint is a point at either end of a line segment. It is also the starting point of a ray.
4	face		A face is a flat surface of a three-dimensional shape.
4	flip		A flip is a kind of movement of a shape. In a flip, a shape is moved to a new position. It is flipped over a line so it faces in the opposite direction.
4	hexagonal prism	prisma hexagonal	A hexagonal prism is a three-dimensional shape. It has two bases that are hexagons. It has six faces that are rectangles.
4	hexagonal pyramid	pirámide hexagonal	A hexagonal pyramid is a three-dimensional shape. Its base is a hexagon. It has six faces that are triangles.

Teacher's Tips

The words *face* and *net* have multiple meanings. Find out what students think each term means. When possible, relate the precise math meaning to one that students already know.

Grade	English	Spanish Cognate	Definition
4	horizontal	horizontal	Horizontal is the direction from left to right.
4	line symmetry	simetría lineal	Line symmetry is what a shape has if it can be folded about a line so that its two parts match exactly.
4	net		A net is a flat pattern. You can fold a net to make a solid shape.
4	pentagonal prism	prisma pentágonal	A pentagonal prism is a three-dimensional shape. It has two bases that are pentagons. It has five faces that are rectangles.
4	pentagonal pyramid	pirámide pentágonal	A pentagonal pyramid is a three-dimensional shape. It has one base that is a pentagon. It has five faces that are triangles.
4	plane	plano	A plane is a flat surface. It extends without end in all directions.
4	pyramid	pirámide	A pyramid is a three-dimensional shape. Its base is a polygon. Its other faces are triangles. The triangles meet at a common vertex.
4	rectangular pyramid	pirámide rectangular	A rectangular pyramid is a three-dimensional shape. It has one base that is a rectangle. It has four faces that are triangles.
4	reflection (flip)	reflexión	A reflection is a kind of movement of a shape. In a reflection, a shape is moved to a new position. It is flipped over a line so it faces in the opposite direction.
4	reflex angle	ángulo reflexivo	A reflex angle measures greater than 180° and less than 360°.
4	rotation (turn)	rotación	A rotation is a kind of movement of a shape. In a rotation, a shape is moved to a new position by rotating the shape around a point.
4	rotational symmetry	simetría rotacional	A shape has rotational symmetry if, after it is turned less than 360° about a central point, it still looks the same in at least two positions.

Teacher's Tips

Homophones like *plane* can be confusing to students. Write the words so students can see the difference in the spellings and help them learn to use context clues to derive meaning and reduce confusion when the word is spoken.

Grade	English	Spanish Cognate	Definition
4	slide		A slide is a kind of movement of a shape. In a slide, a shape is moved to a new position along a straight line. The shape does not change.
4	solid shape		A solid shape is a three-dimensional shape.
4	tessellation	teselación	A tesselation is a kind of repeating pattern. In the pattern, closed shapes cover a surface. There are no gaps or overlaps.
4	three-dimensional	tridimensional	Something that is three-dimensional is measured in three directions. Its length, width, and height are measured.
4	transformation	transformación	A transformation is a movement of a shape. The movements are translation, reflection, or rotation.
4	translation	traslación	A translation is a kind of movement of a shape. In a translation, a shape is moved to a new position along a straight line. The shape does not change.
4	triangular prism	prisma triangular	A triangular prism is a three-dimensional shape. It has two bases that are triangles. It has three faces that are rectangles.
4	triangular pyramid	pirámide triangular	A triangular pyramid is a three-dimensional shape. It has one base that is a triangle. It has three faces that are triangles.
4	turn		A turn is a kind of movement of a shape. In a turn, a shape is moved to a new position by rotating the shape around a point.
4	two-dimensional	bidimensional	Something that is two-dimensional is measured in two directions. Its length and width are measured.
4	vertical	vertical	Vertical is a direction. It is the direction from top to bottom.
5	corresponding angles	ángulos correspondientes	Corresponding angles are angles that are in congruent or similar figures. They are in the same relative position in the different figures.
5	corresponding sides		Corresponding sides are sides that are in congruent or similar figures. They are in the same relative position in the different figures.

Grade	English	Spanish Cognate	Definition
5	decagonal prism		A decagonal prism is a three-dimensional shape. It has two bases that are decagons. It has ten faces that are rectangles.
5	edge		An edge is the line segment that is formed when two faces of a solid figure meet.
5	general quadrilateral	cuadrilátero en general	A general quadrilaterial is a kind of polygon. It has four sides and four angles.
5	heptagon	heptágono	A heptagon is a kind of polygon. A heptagon has seven sides and seven angles.
5	kite		A kite is a quadrilateral. It has exactly two pairs of congruent sides that are next to each other. A kite has no parallel sides.
5	lateral face		A lateral face is part of a polyhedron. It is any surface other than the base.
5	nonagon	eneágono	A nonagon is a polygon. It has nine sides and nine angles.
5	polyhedron	poliedro	A polyhedron is a solid figure. Its faces are polygons.
5	prism	prisma	A prism is a solid figure. It has two congruent, polygon-shaped bases. Its other faces are all rectangles.

81

ALGEBRA VOCABULARY

Use the EL definitions with students to help them understand math terms related to algebra. The terms are organized by grade level so teachers can find vocabulary that applies to their students. For grade 4, students should also use grade 3 vocabulary. For grade 5, students should also use grade 3 and grade 4 vocabulary. For grade 6, students should use grade 3, grade 4, and grade 5 vocabulary.

Grade	English	Spanish Cognate	Definition
3	equation	ecuación	An equation is a number sentence. It has an equal sign. It shows that two quantities are equal.
3	expression	expresión	An expression is part of a number sentence. It has numbers and operation signs. However, it does not have an equal sign.
3	growing pattern		In a growing pattern, the number or number of figures increases by the same amount each time.
3	number sentence		A number sentence includes numbers, operation symbols, and a greater than symbol, a less than symbol, or an equal sign.
3	pattern	patrón	A pattern is an ordered set of numbers or objects. The order helps you predict what will come next.
3	pattern unit	unidad de patrón	The pattern unit is part of a pattern. It is the part that repeats.
3	repeating pattern		A repeating pattern is a kind of pattern. It uses the same pattern unit over and over again.
3	rule		A rule is a kind of instruction. It tells you the correct way to do something.
3	sequence		To sequence events is to write them in order.
3	time line		A time line is a kind of drawing. It shows when events took place. It also shows the order in which they took place.
3	variable	variable	A variable is part of an algebraic expression. It is a letter or a symbol. It stands for an unknown number.
4	algebraic expression	expresión algebraica	An algebraic expression is an expression that includes at least one variable.

Teacher's Tips

Terms like *expression/expresión*, *formula/fórmula*, *function/función*, and *solution/solución* are cognates. If students are familiar with the Spanish term, help them relate it to the English term by pointing out similarities and differences between the Spanish word and the English word.

Grade	English	Spanish Cognate	Definition
4	formula	fórmula	A formula is a set of symbols. It expresses a mathematical rule.
4	function	función	A function is a relationship between two quantities. One quantity depends on the other.
4	function table	tabla de función	A function table matches each input value with an output value. The output values are determined by the function.
4	input/output table		An input/output table is a table that matches each input value with an output value. The output values are determined by the pattern or function.
4	parentheses	paréntesis	Parentheses are symbols. They are used in an expression. They show which operations should be done first.
5	Addition Property of Equality	propiedad de suma de la igualdad	This property states that if you add the same number to both sides of an equation, the sides remain equal.
5	Division Property of Equality	propiedad de división de la igualdad	This property states that if you divide both sides of an equation by the same nonzero number, the sides remain equal.
5	evaluate	evaluar	To evaluate is to find the value of a numerical or algebraic expression.
5	inequality		An inequality is a mathematical sentence. It contains the symbols $<$, $>$, $\le$, $\ge$, or $\ne$.
5	Multiplication Property of Equality	propiedad de multiplicación de la igualdad	This property states that if you multiply both sides of an equation by the same number, the sides remain equal.
5	order of operations	orden de las operaciones	The order of operations is a set of rules. They tell the order in which calculations are done in an expression.
5	solution	solución	A solution is a value in an equation. When the solution is substituted for the variable, it makes an equation true.
5	Substitution Property of Equality	propiedad de sustitución de la igualdad	This property states that if you have one quantity equal to another, you can substitute that quantity for the other in an equation.
5	Subtraction Property of Equality	propiedad de resta de la igualdad	This property states that if you subtract the same number from both sides of an equation, the sides remain equal.

DATA & PROBABILITY VOCABULARY

Use the EL definitions with students to help them understand math terms related to data and probability.
The terms are organized by grade level so teachers can find vocabulary that applies to their students. For grade 4,
students should also use grade 3 vocabulary. For grade 5, students should also use grade 3 and grade 4 vocabulary.
For grade 6, students should use grade 3, grade 4, and grade 5 vocabulary.

Grade	English	Spanish Cognate	Definition
3	bar graph	gráfica de barras	A bar graph is a kind of graph. It uses bars to show data.
3	combination	combinación	A combination is a choice of items. In this choice, the order of the items does not matter.
3	data	datos	Data is information collected about people or things.
3	experiment	experimento	An experiment is a test. The purpose of the test is to find out something.
3	frequency table	tabla de frecuencia	A frequency table is a way to record data. It uses numbers to show how often something happens.
3	horizontal bar graph	gráfica de barras horizontales	A horizontal bar graph is a kind of graph. The bars on the graph go from left to right.
3	key		The key is a part of a map or a graph. The key explains the symbols used.
3	line plot		A line plot is a way to show data. It is a graph. It shows frequency of data along a number line.
3	pictograph	pictografía	A pictograph is a kind of graph. It uses pictures to show and compare information.
3	results	resultados	Results are the answers from a survey.
3	scale	escala	The series of numbers placed at fixed distances on a graph is a scale. The scale helps to label the graph.
3	survey		A survey is a way of gathering information.
3	tally table		A tally table is a way to record data. Tally marks are used to record the data.
3	tree diagram		A tree diagram is an organized list. The list shows all the possible outcomes of an event.
3	Venn diagram	diagrama de Venn	A Venn diagram shows relationships. The relationships are among sets of things.
3	vertical bar graph	gráfica de barras verticales	A vertical bar graph is a kind of graph. The bars on the graph go from bottom to top.
4	frequency	frecuencia	Frequency is the number of times an event occurs.
5	continuous data	datos continuos	Continuous data is data that can be measured and broken down into intervals of time and still have meaning.

Grade	English	Spanish Cognate	Definition
5	coordinate grid		A coordinate grid is a grid formed with a vertical line and a horizontal line. The horizontal line is called the x-axis. The vertical line is called the y-axis.
5	discrete data	datos discretos	Discrete data has a countable number of values. It can be classified into categories.
5	double-bar graph	gráfica de doble barra	A double bar graph is a kind of graph. It uses two bars to compare two similar kinds of data.
5	increment	incremento	An increment is used in graphing. It is the difference between one number and the next on the scale of a graph.
5	interval	intervalo	An interval is used in graphing. It is the difference between one number and the next on the scale of a graph.
5	line graph	gráfica lineal	A line graph is a kind of graph. It uses line segments to show how data change over time.
5	ordered pair	par ordenado	An ordered pair is the set of numbers used to locate a point on a grid. The first number tells the left-right position. The second number tells the up-down position.
5	origin	origen	The origin is a point. It is the point at which two axes of a coordinate plane intersect.
5	trend	trendencia	A trend is a pattern shown in a graph. It shows a pattern over time. In a trend, the data increase, decrease, or stay the same.
5	x-axis		The x-axis is a horizontal number line. It is part of a coordinate plane.
5	x-coordinate	coordenada x	The x-coordinate is the first number in an ordered pair. It tells the distance to move right or left from (0,0).
5	y-axis		The y-axis is a vertical number line. It is part of a coordinate plane.
5	y-coordinate	coordenada y	The y-coordinate is the second number in an ordered pair. It tells the distance to move up or down from (0,0).

Teacher's Tips

Students may confuse the terms *line plot* and *line graph* because both terms include the word *line*. In Spanish the distinction between the two terms is much clearer: a line plot could be translated as *diagrama de puntos*, whereas a line graph is *gráfica lineal*.

Name _____

Name _____

Look at each pattern. Draw or write what comes next in the pattern.

1. ▲▲□▲▲□▲▲□▲▲□▲▲□ _____

2. 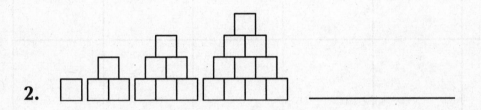 _____

3. ○✪○○✪○○✪ _____

4. ○●□■◇◆⇧⬆☆ _____

5. 🔺 🔺🔺 🔺🔺🔺 🔺🔺🔺 _____

6. 4, 8, 12, 16, 20 _____

7. 100, 90, 80, 70, 60 _____

8. 1, 2, 4, 8, 16 _____

9. 112, 104, 96, 88, 80 _____

10. 25, 5, 50, 10, 100, 20 _____

Name _____

Calendar for the month of _____

	Sunday	Monday	Tuesday	Wednesday	Thursday	Friday	Saturday

Name _____

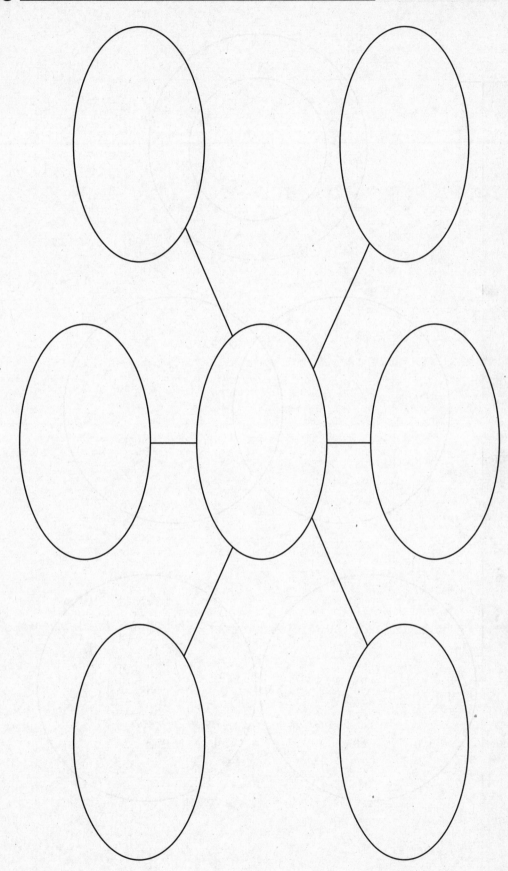

89

Name _____

A.

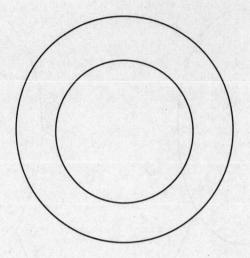

B.

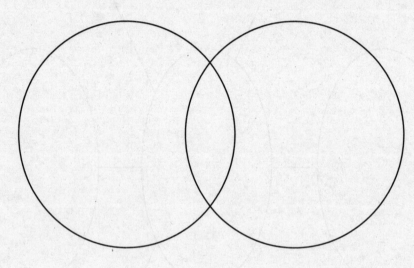

C.

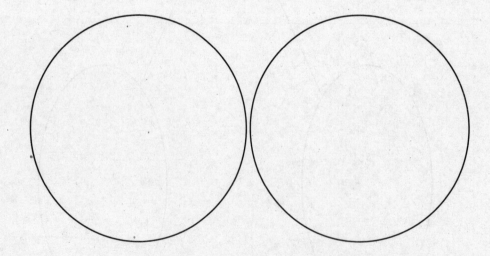

Name _____

Circle the words that are measurements of time.

Word Bank					
day	hour	minute	month	week	year

```
Q  y  M  G  E  Q  K  M
P  W  O  y  E  A  R  B
B  P  N  H  O  U  R  X
M  D  T  J  H  W  A  C
S  A  H  P  U  E  A  I
B  y  N  K  O  E  J  S
P  J  N  T  Q  K  F  B
M  I  N  U  T  E  F  Z
```

Complete each sentence with a word from the word search.

1. There are 60 seconds in a _____ .

2. There are 60 minutes in an _____ .

3. There are 24 hours in a _____ .

4. There are often 30 days in a _____ .

5. There are 7 days in each _____ .

6. There are usually 365 days in a _____ .

Name _____

2	4	1	2
6	8	3	4
10	12	5	6
14	16	7	8
18	20	9	10

Name _____

$\dfrac{4}{4}$	$8 \div 4$	1	2
$5 + 4 - 6$	2×2	3	4
$20 \div 4$	$2 + 2 + 2$	5	6
$10 - 3$	$\dfrac{1}{2}$ of 16	7	8
$20 - 11$	$50 - 40$	9	10

Name _____

	A	B	C	D	E	F
1	12	142	1	14	247	41
2	98	89	2	18	386	187
3	133	341	3	139	310	300
4	1,697	12,578	1,000	21,998	1,062	9,179
5	14,765	5,990	51,000	75,750	4,465	80,985
6	8,677	610	68	86	609	6,731
7	9,875	897	989	99	911	9,610
8	5,695	165	52	25	375	1,005
9	4,312	572	12	21	542	2,029
10	11,306	12,810	21,909	89,992	11,000	31,101

Name _____

Decimals

	A	B	C	D	E	F
1	1.4	1.42	4	41	24.7	4.4
2	8,547.06	54.6	68.006	86	2.06	687.61
3	0.87	8.9	0.8	18.9	38.6	1.87
4	9,872	8.009	78.319	99.9	7.119	9,660.9
5	321	133	139	3	213	2,300
6	4,690.5	16.5	52	2.51	3.75	1,005
7	1,697	32.051	1,000	1,998.1	106.01	9,171
8	4,332	372	12	21	542	2,029
9	15,765	5,990	51.100	76,750	4,351	50,985
10	103.06	21,909	815.02	89,992	11.105	3,110.1

Name _____

Word Bank			
circle	hexagon	octagon	parallelogram
pentagon	rectangle	square	triangle

1 Down	2 Down	3 Down	4 Down
5 Across	**6 Down**	**7 Across**	**8 Across**

Name _____

Word Bank			
circle	hexagon	octagon	pentagon
rectangle	square	trapezoid	triangle

ACROSS

5. 3-sided shape

7. 8-sided shape

8. round shape with
no angles

DOWN

1. 6-sided shape

2. 5-sided shape

3. 4-sided shape with 1 pair of parallel sides

4. 4-sided shape with 2 pairs of parallel sides

6. rectangle with 4 equal sides

Name _____

Word Bank			
centimeter	decimeter	gram	kilogram
kilometer	liter	meter	milliliter

1 Down dm	**2 Down** m	**3 Down** km	**4 Across** mL
_____	_____	_____	_____
5 Down L	**6 Down** g	**7 Across** cm	**8 Across** kg
_____	_____	_____	_____

ACROSS

2. < ____ than

5. ÷

6. ×

7. −

DOWN

1. > ____ than

3. =

4. +

Name _____

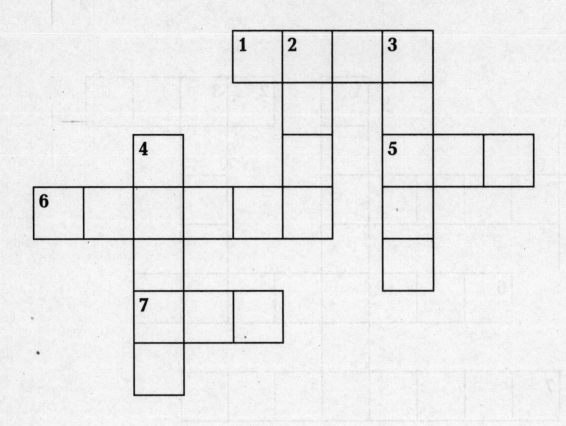

ACROSS

1. A line ___ shows the frequency of data on a number line.

5. A graph with colored rectangles is a ___ graph.

6. A ___ graph helps us compare the parts to the whole.

7. A ___ chart is another name for a circle graph.

DOWN

2. A ___ graph helps us see how data change over time.

3. A tally ___ can be used to record data.

4. When lines connect dots that represent specific data, we have a line ___ .

Crossword Puzzle: Customary Unit Abbreviations

Name ______________________________

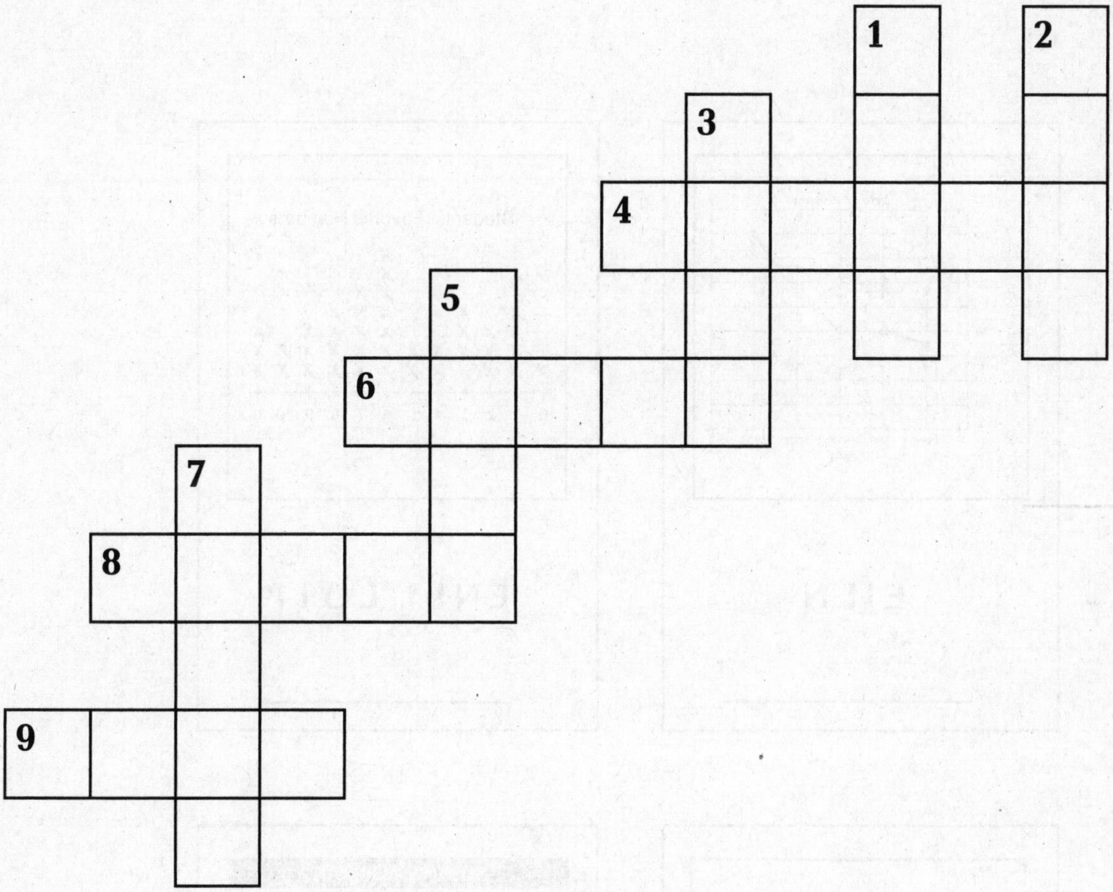

Across

4. gal

6. lb

8. qt

9. in.

Down

1. mi

2. pt

3. yd

5. ft

7. oz

Name _____

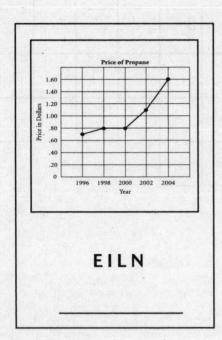

EILN

_____

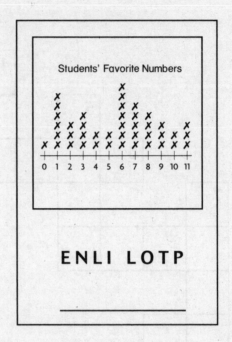

ENLI LOTP

_____

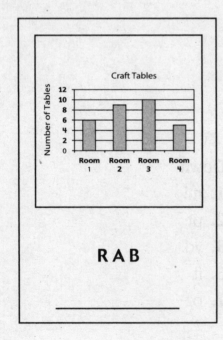

RAB

_____

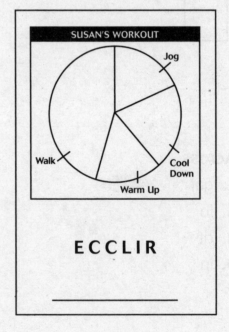

ECCLIR

_____

Name _____

The word	Makes me think of
Definition	**Sentence**

The word	Makes me think of
Definition	**Sentence**

The word	Makes me think of
Definition	**Sentence**

The word	Makes me think of
Definition	**Sentence**

Name _____

Look at each pattern. Draw or write what comes next in the pattern.

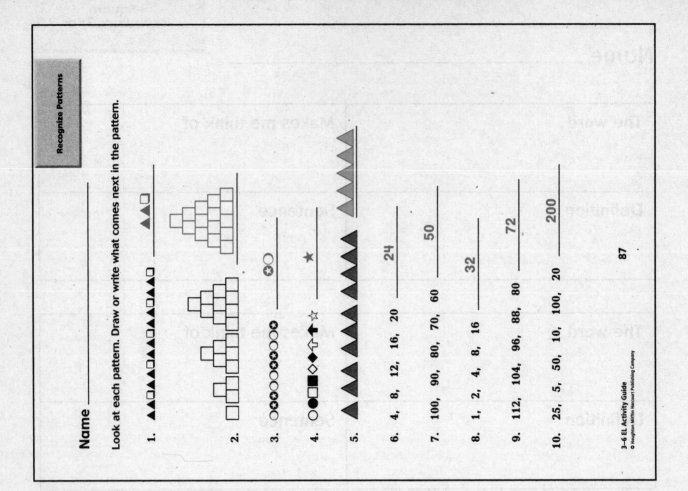

6. 4, 8, 12, 16, 20 _____

7. 100, 90, 80, 70, 60 _____ 50

8. 1, 2, 4, 8, 16 _____ 32

9. 112, 104, 96, 88, 80 _____ 72

10. 25, 5, 50, 10, 100, 20 _____ 200

Name _____

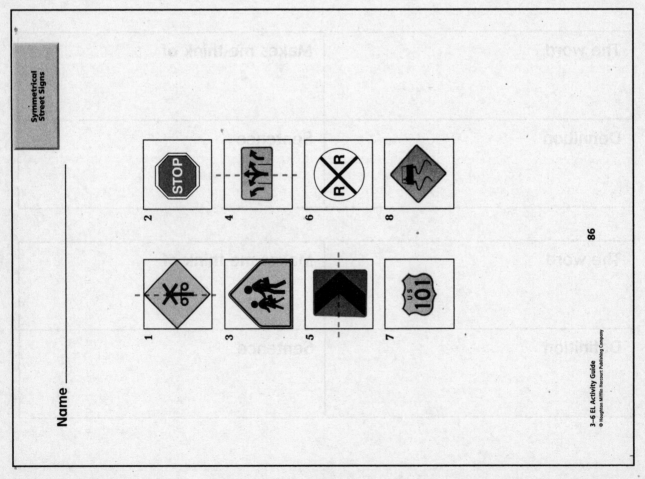

Name _____

	A	B	C	D	E	F
1	12	(142)	1	14	(247)	(41)
2	(98)	89	2	(18)	386	187
3	133	(341)	3	139	(310)	(300)
4	(1,697)	12,578	(1,000)	(21,998)	(1,062)	9,179
5	(14,765)	5,990	51,000	75,750	(4,465)	(80,985)
6	(8,677)	(610)	68	86	(609)	6,731
7	(9,875)	897	989	99	911	(9,610)
8	5,695	165	(52)	25	375	1,005
9	(4,312)	(572)	(12)	21	(542)	2,029
10	(11,306)	12,810	(21,909)	89,992	(11,000)	(31,101)

Name _____

Circle the words that are measurements of time.

		Word Bank			
day	hour	minute	month	week	year

```
Q Y M G E Q K M
P W O Y E A R B
B P N H O U R X
M D T J H W A C
S A H P U E A I
B V N K O E J S
P J N T Q K F B
M I N U T E F Z
```

Complete each sentence with a word from the word search.

1. There are 60 seconds in a __minute__ .

2. There are 60 minutes in an __hour__ .

3. There are 24 hours in a __day__ .

4. There are often 30 days in a __month__ .

5. There are 7 days in each __week__ .

6. There are usually 365 days in a __year__ .

Name _____

Decimals

	A	B	C	D	E	F
1	1.4	1.42	4	(41)	24.7	4.4
2	(8,547.06)	54.6	68.006	86	(2.06)	687.61
3	0.87	(8.9)	0.8	(18.9)	(38.6)	1.87
4	9,872	(8.009)	(78.319)	99.9	(7.119)	9,660.9
5	(321)	133	139	3	213	(2,300)
6	(4,690.5)	(16.5)	52	(2.51)	3.75	1,005
7	(1,697)	32.051	(1,000)	(1,998.1)	106.01	9,171
8	(4,332)	372	(12)	21	(542)	2,029
9	15,765	5,990	(51.100)	(76,750)	(4,351)	50,985
10	(103.06)	21,909	(815.02)	89,992	11.105	3,110.1

95

3-6 EL Activity Guide
© Houghton Mifflin Harcourt Publishing Company

Name _____

Crossword Puzzle: Identify Plane Shapes

Word Bank

circle	hexagon	octagon	parallelogram
pentagon	rectangle	square	triangle

1 Down: CIRCLE
2 Down: RECTANGLE
3 Down: PARALLELOGRAM
4 Down: OCTAGON
5 Across: HEXAGON
6 Down: TRIANGLE
7 Across: PENTAGON
8 Across: SQUARE

96

3-6 EL Activity Guide
© Houghton Mifflin Harcourt Publishing Company

3-6 EL Activity Guide
© Houghton Mifflin Harcourt Publishing Company

106

Crossword Puzzle: Metric Unit Abbreviations

Word Bank

centimeter	decimeter	gram	kilogram
kilometer	liter	meter	milliliter

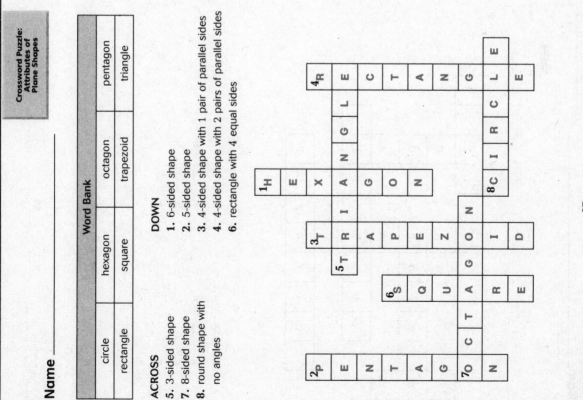

1 Down	2 Down	3 Down	4 Across
dm	m	km	mL
decimeter	meter	kilometer	milliliter

5 Down	6 Down	7 Across	8 Across
L	g	cm	kg
liter	gram	centimeter	kilogram

Crossword Puzzle: Attributes of Plane Shapes

Word Bank

circle	hexagon	octagon	pentagon
rectangle	square	trapezoid	triangle

ACROSS

5. 3-sided shape
7. 8-sided shape
8. round shape with no angles

DOWN

1. 6-sided shape
2. 5-sided shape
3. 4-sided shape with 1 pair of parallel sides
4. 4-sided shape with 2 pairs of parallel sides
6. rectangle with 4 equal sides

Name _____

ACROSS

1. A line ___ shows the frequency of data on a number line.
5. A graph with colored rectangles is a ___ graph.
6. A ___ graph helps us compare the parts to the whole.
7. A ___ chart is another name for a circle graph.

DOWN

2. A ___ graph helps us see how data change over time.
3. A tally ___ can be used to record data.
4. When lines connect dots that represent specific data, we have a line ___.

Name _____

ACROSS

2. < ___ than
5. ÷
6. ×
7. −

DOWN

1. > ___ than
3. =
4. +

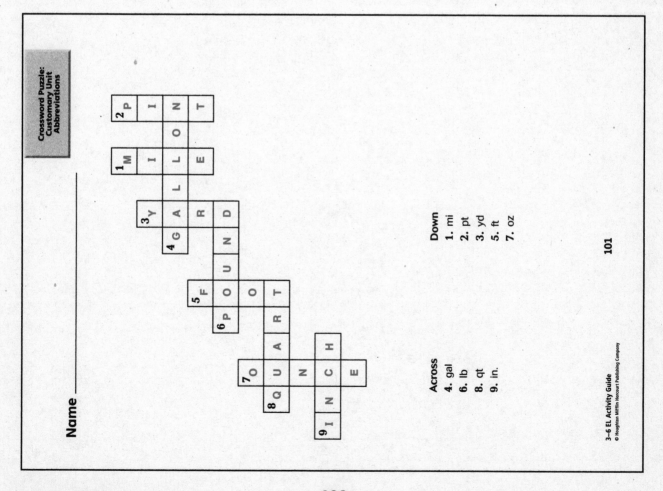

Name _____

Students' Favorite Numbers

E N L I L O T P

LINE PLOT

Price of Progress

E I L N

LINE

SUSAN'S WORKOUT

Jog
Cool Down
Warm Up
Walk

E C C L I R

CIRCLE

Craft Tables
Number of Tables
Room 1 Room 2 Room 3 Room 4

R A B

BAR

3–6 EL Activity Guide
© Houghton Mifflin Harcourt Publishing Company

Name _____

Across
4. gal
6. lb
8. qt
9. in.

Down
1. mi
2. pt
3. yd
5. ft
7. oz

3–6 EL Activity Guide
© Houghton Mifflin Harcourt Publishing Company